MACROBIOTICS REVISITED

A Review of Macrobiotic Theory and Practice

Bob Ligon

George Ohsawa Macrobiotic Foundation
Chico, California

Other Books from G.O.M.F.

Acid and Alkaline
Acid Alkaline Companion
Basic Macrobiotic Cooking
Basic Macrobiotics
Essential Guide to Macrobiotics
Essential Ohsawa
Food and Intuition, Vol 1 & 2
French Meadows Cookbook
Heaven and Nirvana
Macrobiotic Guidebook for Living
Philosophy of Oriental Medicine
Zen Macrobiotics

Editing, text layout, and design by Carl Ferré

First Edition February 2017

PO Box 3998, Chico, California 95927-3998
530-566-9765; gomf@ohsawamacrobiotics.com
www.OhsawaMacrobiotics.com

Published with the help of East West Center for Macrobiotics
www.EastWestMacrobiotics.com

ISBN 978-0-918860-76-7

Preface

My personal journey with macrobiotics began on a hotel rooftop in Kathmandu, Nepal. Watching a beautiful sunset one evening in the spring of 1980, a bearded young man approached and sat down. After a few words of small talk, he launched into an explanation of brown rice and miso soup. He took out a piece of paper, drew a line on it, and put yin on one end and yang on the other. He proceeded to give me my first lesson in macrobiotic theory and practice. I came away from that first exposure to macrobiotics with the title of a book to read later, *The Book of Macrobiotics* by Michio Kushi.

That visit to Nepal was in the middle of a year and a half of open-ended travel throughout Southeast Asia, India, and Nepal. During that time I met many people from many countries and I collected quite a list of book titles, places, and many other wonderful ideas to look into one day. When I returned home to the United States, *The Book of Macrobiotics* was not the first book that I bought. I went into a natural food store in my hometown of Edwardsville, Illinois and looked in the book section. There was this little book about the size of the palm of your hand titled *Zen Macrobiotics*, a book written by the modern day promoter of macrobiotics George Ohsawa. Strange name I thought—combination of a Western given name and a Japanese surname. The title *Zen Macrobiotics* appealed to me in particular because I had lived in Japan for several years as an English teacher and had dabbled in Zen Buddhism studies before going to India and Nepal. This little book fit in my hand so easily that I took it home and devoured it.

Many of the ideas contained in *Zen Macrobiotics* seemed wild, even crazy; but, I couldn't put it down. I couldn't turn away from the passion that was in those pages. Throughout the book there was this thread of correctness that was shaking the foundation of my orientation in life. There are many specific details in *Zen Macrobiotics*, but I found a guiding thought that changed my life forever.

One day, during the time that I worked at the George Ohsawa Macrobiotic Foundation (GOMF), I was walking down the hallway to the kitchen and co-founder Herman Aihara approached me. I stopped and we talked about something superficial when out of the blue Herman said, "What do you get from Ohsawa?" Talk about being put on the spot. One could cite hundreds of ideas, practices, or views of life. What came out was, "Freedom," I said. My reading of Ohsawa's writings and listening to Herman's stories about Ohsawa ultimately seem to point to freedom. As I looked over the text of *Zen Macrobiotics* again recently, one line jumped off the page, "learn to judge, think, and understand with clarity and freedom." pg. 2

That line, "learn to judge, think, and understand with clarity and freedom" simply states one of macrobiotics' greatest contributions to humanity. Utilizing that concept enables an understanding of the macrobiotic conceptualization of the order of the universe and all its myriad manifestations, including a potentially healing and healthy dietary practice. That simple line has been my guiding thought in macrobiotics and in life in general. In any situation, if I'm able to clearly see the truth of the matter and make a decision based on that truth, no matter what the circumstance, then that decision, I believe, will come to good...eventually—be it a physical, emotional, or spiritual concern. Over the years the cultivation of clear judgment, clear thinking, and clear understanding has proven to be helpful and accurate in many areas of life. It is that idea and practice ("learn to judge, think and understand with clarity and freedom") from *Zen Macrobiotics* that is one of the inspirations for this book.

Another inspiration for this book came from my association with Herman Aihara. Herman lived the George Ohsawa instruction to "see for yourself." Herman had the clarity, insight, and courage to make a significant modification and contribution to macrobiotic theory with his ideas on acid and alkaline. George Ohsawa's original formulation was that acid is yin and alkaline is yang. Herman, testing that contention for himself, came up with the idea that acid could be yin or yang, and alkaline could be yin or yang. In what George Ohsawa postulated as a dichotomy, Herman saw a 4-quadrant matrix. It became his signature contribution to macrobiotic thought and continues to this day to inform and assist students of macrobiotics in refining their understanding of diet and lifestyle choices.

Putting these two notions together: "learn to judge, think and understand with clarity and freedom" and "see for yourself" further informs the inspiration and execution of writing this book. I believe this book has been conceived and written in the spirit of George Ohsawa and Herman Aihara and I give those men and their teachings credit for my intellectual inspiration.

Here's one last story about Herman Aihara. In the fall of 1991, Herman approached me and said, "You do magazine?" He spoke in the form of a question, not a command, asking me if I would edit *Macrobiotics Today* magazine. Honored and flattered, I immediately said yes; and, I had the presence of mind to ask a very important question of him. "Do you want me to follow any editorial guidelines in selecting content for the magazine? Are there any subjects or topics that are off limits?" "No," he said. "Just see that it continues." With that he walked away. The latitude that he gave me as editor of *Macrobiotics Today* exemplified the concepts of "freedom" and "see for yourself." He trusted me to carry on the traditions and teachings of George Ohsawa and himself, but with the all-important qualification of doing it as I saw fit. I will be grateful all my days for the trust that Herman placed in me.

– Bob Ligon
January 2017

Introduction

In my work as editor of *Macrobiotics Today*, I remember that Donna Wilson, in her occasional articles, would call for a dialogue among macrobiotic teachers, counselors, and practitioners so that macrobiotics, as a movement or body of information could self-reflect and self-criticize thereby consistently revitalizing the theory and practice. I believe she identified, accurately, that macrobiotics tended to preach to the choir. And as such, macrobiotics did not have a self-revitalizing debate and discussion that could critically consider aspects of theory and practice and propose improvements and changes.

The reason for this book is to offer up some ideas to initiate just such a self-reflection on the theory and practice of macrobiotics. Like many people who have practiced macrobiotics, I have gone through many changes in my relationship to the theory and practice of macrobiotics as I wrote in the Preface.

Macrobiotics, like any system of thought, has certain blind spots that reflect the blind spots of those who have come before us. I know that I have my own blind spots that others will illuminate one day. The task I set out for myself here is to shed light on what I think are some of the areas of macrobiotic theory and practice that could benefit from debate, discussion, and possible modification.

The book is organized in five major sections. Each section and/or chapter highlights the contributions and strengths of a particular area of macrobiotic theory and practice, then moves into reviewing and critiquing that area, and concludes with suggestions for modification that I hope will generate debate and discussion.

Contents

Part 5. Good Judgment and Freedom

Part 1

Yin/Yang Theory

Chapter 1

The Dialectic

Macrobiotics, and more specifically George Ohsawa, has made many contributions to humanity. The notions of gratitude, taking responsibility for one's actions, and the realization of freedom have enriched many lives immeasurably. I refer you to Ohsawa's writings for more details on what these notions embody. Briefly, the philosophical principles put forth by Ohsawa can provide guidance through the chaos of life. These principles make sense of a seemingly random universe and empower the individual with the ability to control her or his own destiny.

George Ohsawa wrote in *Zen Macrobiotics*, it (*macrobiotics*) "is a dialectic conception of the infinite universe." p. 19. The use of a dialectic concept in describing phenomenon is an immensely important contribution of macrobiotics. This notion underlies all of macrobiotic theory and practice. In simple Far Eastern terms, it is the theory of yin and yang. Ages old, this theory can effectively explain the state and dynamics of all phenomenon. Yin/yang is a compass or "magic spectacles" that can guide one in decision making of all kinds. The use of yin and yang makes possible the estimations of appropriateness, from food selection and preparation to the selection of a life direction. Although I will take issue with some of the macrobiotic formulations of yin and yang, the introduction of a dialectic is one of the major contributions of macrobiotic theory.

One basic tenet of macrobiotic theory is that we live in a relative universe where antagonistic forces are in constant flux, yet paradoxically maintain an equilibrium that allows us to exist in an ever-elusive balance. At a sensorial level, we observe up and down, hot and cold, night and day. These are examples of the polarity of the dialectic, here expressed as static extremes.

You might notice that each of these pairs is a relative concept. Take hot and cold for example. In July, when the temperature is 80°F or 90°F you would probably say that 50°F is cold. However, in the dead of winter in February when the temperature could be -5°F, 50°F would seem at least warm if not hot. In this fashion, the dialectic enables us to evaluate the meaning of 50°F. The meaning of 50°F is not absolutely hot or cold, but can have the meaning of hot or cold in relation to a certain environment.

This would seem to be a paradox. How can an idea, notion, or value like 50°F mean two seemingly contradictory things when it looks like it's a singular entity? This is one of the beauties of the dialectic. It enables a deeper understanding than what might be apparent from the surface.

The dialectic cuts through the complexity and confusion of life providing a sense of order in the seeming chaos. There are many macrobiotic books that provide more detailed explanations of this concept. Suffice it to say that, while the dialectic did not originate with macrobiotics, the use of a dialectic is a distinguishing feature of macrobiotic theory and practice.

Chapter 2

Yin and Yang Dynamics

Yin and Yang—Native State

Over the many years of macrobiotic discussions, teaching, writing, and debates, the subject of yin and yang has been given much attention. Rightly so. Yin/yang theory is the basis for macrobiotic theory in particular and for Far Eastern philosophies and medicine in general. The inclusion of a dialectic-like yin/yang is one of the strengths of macrobiotics. While yin/yang theory has many applications in macrobiotics, I have never been able to reconcile several seeming theoretic contradictions.

Macrobiotic theory states that the tendency of yang is contraction and the tendency of yin is expansion. One crucial detail that has never been clarified sufficiently is whether the macrobiotic qualities of yin and yang refer to the native state of something or whether it refers to the resulting effect of yin or yang energy. It would appear from the yin/yang chart shown on page 13 (*The Book of Macrobiotics,* p. 13) that native state is the prevailing condition. All of the "Attributes" seem to me to be native states, that is, what something is without an energy acting upon it.

Yin and yang are not static qualities, but rather a way to refer to relative states or conditions. For example, a carrot is not simply yin or yang, but can be viewed as yin compared to burdock (carrot is not as hard, has more moisture), but it would be yang compared to lettuce (lettuce is a broad leaf, more moisture, and delicate texture). This example uses the native state of carrots, burdock, and lettuce. This characterization is somewhat useful in determining the yin/yang quality of, in this case, a vegetable.

Table 1. Examples of Yin and Yang

	Yin ▼*	Yang ▲*
Attribute	Centrifugal force	Centripetal force
Tendency	Expansion	Contraction
Function	Diffusion	Fusion
	Dispersion	Assimilation
	Separation	Gathering
	Decomposition	Organization
Movement	More inactive, slower	More active, faster
Vibration	Shorter wave and higher frequency	Longer wave and lower frequency
Direction	Ascent and vertical	Descent and horizontal
Position	More outward and peripheral	More inward and central
Weight	Lighter	Heavier
Temperature	Colder	Hotter
Light	Darker	Brighter
Humidity	Wetter	Drier
Density	Thinner	Thicker
Size	Larger	Smaller
Shape	More expansive and fragile	More contractive and harder
Form	Longer	Shorter
Texture	Softer	Harder
Atomic particle	Electron	Proton
Elements	N, O, P, Ca, etc.	H, C, Na, As, Mg, etc.
Environment	Vibration … Air … Water … Earth	
Climatic effects	Tropical climate	Colder climate
Biological	More vegetable quality	More animal quality
Sex	Female	Male
Organ structure	More hollow and expansive	More compacted and condensed
Nerves	More peripheral, orthosympathetic	More central, parasympathetic
Attitude, emotion	More gentle, negative, defensive	More active, positive, aggressive
Work	More psychological and mental	More physical and social
Consciousness	More universal	More specific
Mental function	Dealing more with the future	Dealing more with the past
Culture	More spiritually oriented	More materially oriented
Dimension	Space	Time

* For convenience, the symbols for Yin, and for Yang are used

Yin and Yang—Effect

Confusion sets in when one looks at the effect of yin or yang energy. Referring to the yin/yang chart, yang characteristics are contraction, hotter, brighter, more aggressive, drier, gathering, and male; and, yin characteristics are expansion, colder, darker, more defensive, wetter, separation, and female. Following this categorization of the qualities of yin and yang, male, hot, and bright are all yang characteristics and female, cold, and dark are all yin ones compared to each other respectively.

If yang is hotter and contractive and yin is colder and expansive, then you would expect something that has heat applied to it to contract. Conversely, something that has cold applied to it should expand. To my observation, applying heat to something makes it expand. Water heated creates steam, expanding to the extent that it will drive turbines. Putting food into a refrigerator causes the microbial activity to slow down, retarding spoilage. That slowing down is contracting—reducing activity.

One of the macrobiotic principles is that yang produces yin and yin produces yang. This understanding seemingly resolves the contradiction that heat (yang) causes something to expand (yin) and that cold (yin) causes something to contract (yang). And though macrobiotic theory does state this relationship between yin and yang, it is not explained well enough in macrobiotic books and lectures. This principle leads us to an important question however.

When is yin or yang viewed as a native state and when is it applied as an effect of energetic movement? It seems to me that macrobiotic theory applies yin/yang dynamics in both ways and the result ends up being confusing. My conclusion is that the macrobiotic formulations of yin and yang are not only used in a logically inconsistent way but also have been interpreted by many with yang (male) oriented bias.

I would concede that it may be a matter of perspective and opinion. However, I have a real problem when the macrobiotic version of yin/yang dynamics is applied by macrobiotic counselors or teachers in an attempt to make macrobiotic practice a medical modality.

Despite the usefulness of the macrobiotic formulations of yin/yang in some applications, those same formulations can have significant negative consequences when pressed into service of diagnosis and treatment incorrectly.

An Alternate View

Still utilizing a dialectic approach, it is appealing to view the earth as being composed of matter and energy. Matter and energy are a fundamental relative world polarity. Energy animates matter. For example, electricity (energy) makes appliances (matter) run, otherwise the appliance is just a construction of metal and plastic. Conversely, matter gives form to energy. That same electricity (energy) puts the form of the appliance (matter) in motion; otherwise, electricity is an invisible energy of no use to us. This example helps us make sense how the complementary antagonism of the dualistic, binary material world works.

In this way of thinking, matter can be conceived as yin, and energy can be conceived as yang. This formulation of yin/yang comes from Traditional Chinese Medicine (hereafter TCM), and to my observation, more accurately reflects the nature of the material world.

Yang as the Whole Enchilada

To my understanding, the macrobiotic formulation of yin and yang has both matter and energy as yang characteristics. In macrobiotics, yang is the energetic, the animator, but since yang is thought to be contracting it is also the solid, the heavy, the material, while yin is the expansive and lighter. Yin then, in macrobiotic terms, has little energy and little or no matter. This viewpoint has led to yang being aggrandized by macrobiotic practitioners. It is everything positive, creative, admirable, and desirable. Yang is viewed as the energetic force and it yields all the stuff we see. It is no coincidence that yang is associated with male-ness and that this interpretation of macrobiotic theory heavily favors yang as the quality that is most desired and respected. In addition, macrobiotics comes from Japan, which at that time (early 20th century) was a very patriarchal, hierarchical society and, at least on the surface, was dominated by yang male-ness: authoritarian, militaristic, and aggressive (think of the Japanese invasion and occupation of Manchuria). Ironically, George Ohsawa railed against these very qualities at that time (1930s) because he felt Japanese society was turning toward warmongering.

While I'd grant that the macrobiotic formulations of yin and yang can be useful for cosmological explanations and food energetics and cooking *within* the macrobiotic system, using the skewed version of macrobiotic formulations of yin and yang for health recommendations can result in inaccurate assessments of someone's health condition and subsequently, inappropriate recommendations, particularly dietary recommendations.

There is much that has been said and will be said on this particular topic, but here I'd like to confine my comments to the use of yin and yang in assessing health conditions and my experiences with consultation clients.

About 20 years ago, I was offering macrobiotic consultations while studying TCM in San Diego. I noticed that a significant number of those consultation clients had been practicing a macrobiotic diet and lifestyle for five, ten, and even fifteen years. Furthermore, I observed that many of these people had striking similarities in their conditions. Almost to a person (15 clients in a three month period), he or she showed signs of the TCM diagnosis of chronic Qi and Blood deficiency: pale skin, dry skin and hair, low energy and fatigue, physical weakness, poor mental concentration, cold hands and/or feet, cessation of menstruation, and either weight loss or inability to gain weight. Each individual had developed these symptoms despite eating large volumes of food, following what they thought was a proper macrobiotic diet, and in most cases what another counselor had recommended.

At first I thought it was a strange coincidence, but after the ninth and tenth case I began to see a pattern. After careful thought, I noticed a gap in the way macrobiotic theory of yin/yang dynamics is taught and presented in macrobiotic lectures and books that might likely explain this pattern and the conditions of these clients.

Yang—Good; Yin—Bad

In many macrobiotic books, classes, and lectures, yang qualities, yang food, and yang energy have been positively emphasized, with yin being passed off as inferior, weak, and the energy to be feared. "Oh don't eat that cookie, it's too yin." "I'm not allowed to eat any fruit, the books say fruit is bad." That last comment is not actually true. The books don't specifically say that fruit is bad, but with the almost universal connotation that yang is good and yin is bad, the overwhelmingly common impression among macrobiotic students over the years is that yin is bad and to be avoided, and that it might even cause cancer.

I used to think this was a prejudice among teachers, but more accurately, I think it is built into macrobiotic culture, even if it is not specifically codified in macrobiotic theory. Despite the moderate presentation of "emphasized" foods such as brown rice and "less emphasized" foods like fruit, what the average neophyte macrobiotic student would hear is brown rice "good" fruit "bad." My guess and my own memory of my early days studying macrobiotics is that it was the tone of writings and the personality of teachers that led people to such a judgmental interpretation of food selection. The "daily" foods were good, and in the spirit of the American love for excess, more was always better. The "occasional" foods were bad, and true to the love of excess, if a small amount is all that's allowed, then none at all must be better.

I remember Herman Aihara saying that George Ohsawa was surprised how literal Americans were. The story would go something like this. Ohsawa used a samurai-style of teaching, somewhat bombastic, putting students on the spot with questions like "Why is a honeycomb a hexagonal shape?" Herman would recount, with affection, that Ohsawa would roundly scold students for incorrect answers, or, to Ohsawa's credit, answers that lacked original critical thinking. Samurai-style is supposed to toughen you up; shake you loose from your complacency and arrogance. Herman would continue that in France, macrobiotic students would sit through the

Samurai-style and then do what they thought was best, not getting side tracked by the intimidating Samurai-style. Americans however, more insecure in themselves, might have quaked at the sound of Ohsawa's basso profundo voice and thus attempted to comply with his pronouncements to the letter. What worked well in France, and perhaps in Japan, had a quite different effect in North America.

The origins of modern-day macrobiotics (early 20th Century), the timing of its arrival in North America (during the hey day of the "Mad Men" era in the 1950s), and the fact that most of the macrobiotic teachers were male, contributed to a culture that influenced many people (unconsciously and quite subtly perhaps) by means of control, dominance, intimidation, and fear.

And then in the 1980s, macrobiotics was hailed as a cure for cancer, with the none-too-subtle subtext, anything "not" macrobiotic might give you cancer. And anything not macrobiotic was anything not on a preferred list. Fruit might cause cancer, any bean except aduki beans might cause cancer, and any animal food...well it was just curtains then. Designating a macrobiotic diet as a cure for cancer sealed its fate as a restrictive and rigid interpretation of macrobiotic dietary principles. That's where the perception that even a slight deviation from the Standard Macrobiotic Diet (a Kushi invention described in the next chapter) might lead to cancer gained support. Then, that interpretation of macrobiotic dietary principles could be used to implant fear in those who violated the dictates of the teachers and counselors thereby preserving the status and authority of teachers and counselors and serving as a bludgeon to tamp down dissent. Thereafter, misguided group-think and group denial took root.

Start with a theory that was interpreted in a logically inconsistent way and not suited to be a medical modality, add the culture of male-ness of the 1930s to1950s and what came down the pike was an approach to diet, lifestyle and health care that was incomplete at best and confusing, chauvinistic, and possibly harmful at worst.

A Different Yin and Yang

An alternate formulation of yin/yang (the TCM version) is that yang is the energetic but is expansive rather than contractive (energy, heat, and movement create expansion); and, yin is matter and contraction rather than expansive (coolness and stillness lead to contraction or condensation).

Using macrobiotic formulations of yin/yang one might conclude incorrectly that energy and matter are yang (both active and contractive). This accounts at least in part, for the development of the deficiency conditions in the longtime macrobiotic practitioners.

If, when one begins to feel deficient, he or she tries to yangize either with food or strenuous exercise, one may increase energy temporarily but will likely consume substance (reserves). And the more one tries to yangize in this fashion, the more one is likely to deplete oneself. This type of condition and degeneration might even have afflicted George Ohsawa himself and many macrobiotic teachers and students.

Since macrobiotic theory conceptualizes yin as expansive there is no polarity between energy and substance, so there is no accommodation in macrobiotic theory for nourishing substance as a complement to energy.

Alternately, the TCM formulations of yin and yang conceptualize energy and substance as complementary qualities. In this system there are very clear signs and symptoms (essentially those listed in the example above) that indicate substance deficiency. Because a polarity exists between energy and substance, the course of treatment or diet when substance deficiency appears is to nourish substance (the yin of the TCM) and not to increase yang. This approach will build substance and not excessively increase yang (which would further deplete yin/substance).

In my opinion even the most careful assessment of someone's condition using macrobiotic theory will inherently be in error and will result in a fairly serious imbalance over time. I still might not have believed this if it weren't my own experience of trying to use macrobiotic theory some 15 years for dietary and lifestyle guidance and developing similar deficiency symptoms as my clients.

Furthermore, this line of inquiry gave me an explanation as to why some longtime macrobiotic practitioners at macrobiotic gatherings looked pale, gaunt, and weak despite eating huge mounds of brown rice, vegetables, and miso soup. A further extension of TCM theory of yin and yang would explain those gaunt looking people as having lost both substance (from years of inadequate nutrition) and energy (over time with a continual lack of substance there isn't enough substance to fuel energy, so energy also declines). Without enough substance, energy is depleted, without enough energy, food cannot be converted to blood and tissue. The result over time is a chronic deficiency condition of both substance and energy developing in a degenerative spiral.

Chapter 3

The Standard Macrobiotic Diet

Cultural Developments

In addition to the inherent contradictions in macrobiotic theory concerning yin/yang, there was a sequence of unique cultural developments over many years that further skewed macrobiotic theory into an unworkable system of diagnosis and treatment. George Ohsawa himself was a very active individual, you might say yang in the macrobiotic sense. He was outspoken, aggressive, and very energetic. When he came to United States late in 1959, I imagine he saw a population of people that were quite different from those in Japan. After World War II, scarcity was the rule in Japan. The population there had to scramble to survive, even to find enough to eat. Likely, there were not very many overweight people in Japan at that time. Indeed, the traditional historical Japanese diet is generally low in fat, high in carbohydrates, vegetables, sea vegetables, fermented vegetables, and miso, and not a diet that is likely to promote overweight people. Furthermore, Japanese culture traditionally is not confrontational on a social level. Politeness is the rule. While aggressive behavior, particularly public drunkenness in Japan, might be tolerated, it is not generally the rule.

So when George Ohsawa came to America, likely he saw quite a different character than he would have been accustomed to seeing in Japan or Europe. Europe was also devastated by World War II and scarcity was prevalent there as well. But in America, the post-World War II era was a boom time of materialism and access to almost unlimited food. Foods that had been relatively scarce in America prior to World War II were then abundantly available. Chiefly, what was available in America that was scarce elsewhere was the abundance of animal food and processed food. In America, what had once been considered luxury or novelty foods were now available to a broader spectrum of American society in an unprecedented abundance, and at affordable prices.

After World War II, America was the land of milk and honey, beef and store-bought cookies, frozen TV dinners, white bread, and sugar, sugar, sugar. Naturally, such deprived individuals wanted to make up for lost time and consumed far more then he or she needed. Socially in America, we are still coping with that change of attitude. Since the 1940s obesity has increased and, along with that, there has been an increase of preventable degenerative illnesses such as diabetes, heart disease, cancer, and stroke.

Cooling, Draining, Dispersing, Cleansing

Back in the 1960s these trends were in their early stages. The nutrient dense high-energy dietary choices available might have contributed to the reputation of what is popularly known throughout the world as the "Ugly American." This "Ugly American" is typically male, overweight, often with a barrel chest and big belly, and probably with a red face, loud voice, and aggressive personality. It's my suspicion that this is the type of personality and condition that George Ohsawa met in the 1960s. In response to such a condition George Ohsawa would have applied macrobiotic dietary principles so as to influence these kinds of characters in a positive healthy manner. In so doing George Ohsawa's recommendations for the "Ugly American" type became, under the guidance of Michio Kushi in the late 1970s, the Standard Macrobiotic Diet—a dietary practice codified into books and teaching that emphasizes a cooling, draining, dispersing, cleansing energy.

For someone who is 50 pounds overweight and is having trouble walking because of sore knees and seems irritated at just about anything because there's so much heat and pressure building up inside of him or her, a simple diet of whole grains and vegetables, strange sounding fermented foods like miso, soy sauce, and sea vegetables would very likely (initially) make such a person feel fantastic. Possibly, this was the experience of the early American practitioners of macrobiotics.

Addressing Not Curing

Some of these people who were first exposed to macrobiotics in America were of yang constitutions with excess conditions. The macrobiotic dietary formulations at that time were well-suited for *addressing* those conditions. Note, that I would not say they were well-suited to *curing* those conditions. That is a crucial distinction.

When someone with an excess condition comes to macrobiotics for the first time, and follows the Standard Macrobiotic Diet (as it was commonly taught and written about in the late 1970s and 1980s by Michio Kushi and his students) they will feel different, most likely better. As such, macrobiotics might be viewed as a successful way to promote good health. The standard diet that was taught and practiced at that time (and I think largely up to the present) is a formulation of macrobiotic practices that essentially is appropriate for an excess condition. This formulation includes whole grains, vegetables, beans and sea vegetables, miso soup, pickles, small amounts of other foods, and minimal fat and protein. Energetically speaking, this is a dietary practice that will cool, cleanse, drain, and disperse. Overheated, tight irritable people will be calmer. An overweight person will lose weight. Mucus congestion will disperse. Lung and skin conditions are likely to improve. One might feel lighter and more clearheaded.

After working professionally in macrobiotics for a few years, I began to wonder why macrobiotics had never become more broadly successful. The arrival of George Ohsawa in the 1960s and the subsequent application of macrobiotic dietary principles toward addressing primarily excess conditions, I believe, is at least partly responsible. My rough estimate is that about 15% of people who come to macrobiotics experience success and the majority of these people have excess conditions when they find macrobiotics. People with deficient conditions don't do so well with a standard macrobiotic approach and usually won't stick with it. If one is already weak and has a weak constitution, a cooling, cleansing, draining, dispersing dietary practice likely will make one's condition worse. If people with excess conditions stick with the Standard Macrobiotic Diet long enough, they will likely develop deficient conditions.

It is important to remember that the Standard Macrobiotic Diet is a specific and narrow application of macrobiotic dietary principles. In theory, macrobiotic dietary principles can be applied to any condition to create a customized dietary and lifestyle plan for that condition. The promotion and prevalence of the Standard Macrobiotic Diet is a restrictive dietary practice for excess conditions and obscures the versatility of macrobiotic dietary principles. Following the Standard Macrobiotic Diet is not true macrobiotics.

Personal Experience

I came across macrobiotics when I was 25 years old. At that time I was a Midwestern meat-and-potato, dairy-and-sugar American farm-diet kid. I was probably about 30 pounds overweight and so full of mucus that the first time I tried to stand on my head in a yoga class my head nearly exploded.

I felt wonderful the first eighteen months to three years on the version of a macrobiotic diet I practiced at the time. I had never felt so light and clearheaded in my life. I lost weight. I lost the early beginnings of a beer belly. I initially thought macrobiotics was a panacea of health. And like many before me, I developed a zealous attachment to macrobiotics that resisted all other approaches.

When my health began to deteriorate after about five years, I bought into the notion that it was my fault. I just wasn't eating enough pressure-cooked short grain brown rice. I wasn't cutting my vegetables properly. I wasn't using enough salt in my cooking. I ate too many apples. I had not been a good macrobiotic practitioner. In short, I was blaming myself with no thought that the books, teachers, counselors, or the theory (using the macrobiotic formulations of yin and yang) itself might be inappropriate for me and possibly in error in general. I believe blaming the practitioner was at least unconsciously encouraged by macrobiotic teachers and counselors who were handicapped by a theory that couldn't recognize or appropriately address deficiency conditions.

Double Down

As I got weaker I doubled down. I became even more rigid, careful, or strict. Surely, I thought, if I practice macrobiotics carefully enough I would regain the sense of health, lightness, and energy that I had enjoyed initially. I was more than willing to deny and inaccurately interpret my own biofeedback for the sake of adhering to information and teachings about a dietary practice that was now unhealthy for me.

When I was in the throes of my macrobiotic practice in those early years, no one could tell me anything different from my macrobiotic beliefs, not my parents, friends, or other sources that I would read…they were all wrong. I had the secret to health, happiness, and longevity. I was just going through a rough patch or discharge and one day I would regain the strength and vitality that I had experienced earlier on. But for me, that day never came just with standard macrobiotics.

Without evil intent and as I think now, these are the behaviors of someone in the throes of a cult-like mentality. Ultimately, I have only myself to blame.

A New Day

I have an abiding faith in a benevolent divine energy that guides our lives if we open up to it. Through a series of what seemed like untoward reverses at the time, my working at the Vega Study Center came to an end in 1993. At one time, I thought I would make a career out of macrobiotics. That was not to be. Instead I chose to study TCM. As I stated earlier, the TCM formulations of yin/yang are different than those of macrobiotics. Yet, still I believed in macrobiotics. Even though by this time I had lost weight, had gaunt cheeks, was not sleeping well, had night sweats, and had difficulty concentrating (classic signs of yin deficiency in TCM).

About 1½ years into my study and after seeing three different practitioners of TCM who all told me the same thing, I had an epiphany. I was living and studying in San Diego and went into the new Whole Foods in the Hillcrest neighborhood. I wandered by the meat case with the free-range, organically raised, grass-fed animal food and something inside of me snapped. I bought a pound of bacon, went home, fried it up, and ate every bit of it. The divine had come to my rescue. The sense of relief was indescribable. In denial, I had been suppressing the truth of my condition, attempting to persist in my ineffective beliefs despite all the biofeedback that my health was deteriorating. That was the turning point for me. After that I looked at macrobiotic teachings, books, and the condition of macrobiotic teachers and counselors in a new light.

I don't mean to suggest that anyone else might improve their health by eating bacon. What I want to stress here and throughout this book, is that deciding to eat bacon was an expression of my freedom. I like to think that that decision was the result of developing critical thinking to the degree that I knew what was appropriate for me at that time—this is true application of macrobiotic theory.

George Ohsawa taught that we follow macrobiotic principles with regard to diet and lifestyle so that we may one day be free to eat or do whatever we want in pursuit of our dream and/or purpose. The caveat to that freedom though is responsibility and respect for limitations.

Freedom as Ohsawa taught it is to make choices that stay within one's limits of tolerance. Within those limits we have infinite freedom. My interpretation is that if we respect our limitations, we have fewer distractions from finding our purpose and realizing our dream. People who consistently exceed their limitations over time create imbalances that produce experiences in the physical realm that undeniably get our attention—to the point of distraction. Usually what gets our attention is suffering in the form of seemingly inexplicable illness, injury, accident, or emotional, financial, or physical down turns in life.

Bacon is not the answer for everyone (or anyone other than me as far as I know); rather, the answer is studying, practicing, reflecting, experimenting, and critically thinking to find one's way, whether it is in food choices or questioning yin/yang theory. Clear, creative, critical thinking is at the heart of macrobiotics. And, it was doing all of the above that led me to the opinion that the formulations of yin/ yang in macrobiotics and their application to my diet and lifestyle choices were not yielding the results I was led to expect.

Chapter 4

Macrobiotics is Not a Medical Modality

Desperate Need for Guidance

It is my feeling that George Ohsawa might not have intended to play doctor. To my eye, Ohsawa was a man of big ideas…indeed Big Life or as we know it, macrobiotics. He spoke in broad strokes of cosmology, science, and philosophy. I don't think he cared much for documentation of his ideas. He was so inspired that the ideas gushed out of him with incredible energy. Nevertheless, he tapped a current of need in those he spoke to; and, those who were ill, weak, or disheartened were drawn to him. Herman Aihara often spoke of how broken and lost he was before he found Ohsawa. Once under his instruction and care, Herman began to thrive again and thereafter dedicated his life to teaching and developing macrobiotics.

Those who came to see Ohsawa desperately needed guidance as any of us do when we are lost without a clue. People in such conditions likely implored him to help them. And so it was that he began making recommendations to people with health and other problems. There are reports/stories of people lining up and waiting for hours to see Ohsawa in Japan to hear what he had to offer for them to improve their conditions.

It was his inclination toward big ideas that I believe resulted in a lack of detail or rigor in some areas of macrobiotic theory. Furthermore, a charismatic individual can inspire change in someone merely by force of personality. More than a few times I have witnessed people accept strong conviction as truth without carefully examining what they have been told. Many people would like to be told what to do by a benevolent dominating figure. Life would be so much easier that way. One wouldn't have to think or wrestle with thorny propositions. Someone else could do the thinking and all one would have to do is comply. That to me is the antithesis of macrobiotics. Taking personal responsibility by way of critical thinking, self-reflection, and sober, grounded decision making is essential to achieving health, happiness, or one's purpose and true destiny.

As George Ohsawa wrote in *Zen Macrobiotics* p. 114:

"...In order to achieve a high degree of health and happiness, an individual should:

1. understand through study the order of the universe of which he is a part;
2. learn to be highly aware of himself and his reactions to his environment;
3. think, think, and think all of the time."

That about says it all for macrobiotics, especially #3 "...think, think, and think all the time." Self-awareness, mindfulness, and actively, creatively thinking and acting according to what one knows to be true in one's heart and mind is the path to heaven, nirvana, paradise, enlightenment, and health and happiness on this earth.

I believe macrobiotic teachers, counselors, and keepers of the faith (of whom I count myself as one) have failed to inspire these qualities in their students, clients, and associates.

The Temptation

The temptation for a person in a teaching, counseling position to respond to people's desperate need for guidance by creating a power structure that is dictatorial, prescriptive, inflexible (possibly inaccurate), and capable of subjugating the will of those in need, is irresistible to the human ego. It is possibly an unconscious impulse to dominate and control—to set one's self up as an authority figure and not endure any challenge to that authority, all the while believing it is done to help people. What this can lead to is an arrogant belief in one's own righteousness. I've often heard, from TCM patients recounting their experiences with macrobiotics, what sounds like efforts at intimidation by counselors and teachers to evade reflection on the correctness of their recommendations. At the same time, macrobiotic counselors and teachers think they are doing what is right and best. The problem is a fundamental gap in macrobiotic teaching, the unworkable theory of yin/yang as it is applied to health recommendations.

Cultural Influence

To be fair, I believe there is another cultural factor that contributed to this development in macrobiotics. In Japan, the apprentice/student never questioned the master, even if he disagreed or knew something was not right. It just wasn't done. There was a strong influence of this cultural characteristic on macrobiotics that carried over from George Ohsawa's first Japanese students to the first American students. It is interesting to note that an idea that goes unquestioned after a couple of generations may become accepted as truth without question. There has been some of this at work in macrobiotics.

The result, at least in the culture of macrobiotics in North America, was a set of teachers, counselors, writers, and practitioners who developed and taught a macrobiotic dogma with "do" and "don't" lists, and perpetuated an imperious domination of students and counseling clients. Anyone voicing dissent, questioning senior teachers, or criticizing macrobiotic theory was/is likely to be rejected, shamed, or ostracized. And when you have made a commitment to a professional career based on that dogma and style of teaching/counseling, the threat of ostracism is powerfully persuasive to toe the party line.

What developed in this environment was for macrobiotic teachers/counselors (perhaps unconsciously) to set themselves up as nearly god-like figures. He (mostly), but she as well, became someone who had all the answers, was (nearly) always right, and was duty-bound to preserve the purity of the dogma, and set the heretics straight or boot them out altogether. Thoughtful creative investigation and critique was not, could not, be tolerated and what emerged was a cult-like organization of unquestioned leaders and unquestioning followers. A codependence developed in which the leaders were always consolidating and preserving their power, and followers were subjugated and disempowered.

As this kind of subculture developed over the years, macrobiotic counselors and teachers might have begun to view themselves as healthcare practitioners. Instead of remaining a support modality aimed at establishing and maintaining a sound basis from which health could be improved, macrobiotics developed a culture of diagnosis and treatment. And that, to me, was an overreach at least and, at worst, a grave error.

The individual details of diagnosis that were taught in macrobiotic diagnosis were not entirely incorrect. The crucial flaw or omission was that there wasn't a coherent system of diagnosis and treatment to integrate all the details of diagnosis.

It wasn't until I was two years into my study of TCM that I realized that macrobiotic diagnosis methods were unreliable. Again, not because the individual pronouncements were incorrect, but because one sign or symptom does not a diagnosis make. What I learned in TCM was that no one sign or symptom can lead to a clear diagnosis. What the TCM system does that a macrobiotic approach does not, is to look for a pattern of signs and symptoms. The TCM system has developed and has been refined to the point that if signs and symptoms are collected and a pattern is discerned, then a reliable differential diagnosis can be determined. That means that a practitioner can focus very specifically on treating someone's condition with the treatment methods that are paired to that differential diagnosis. That kind of specificity provides a reliable means to treat all manner of conditions. That is a healthcare treatment modality.

In addition to a differential diagnosis and customized treatment plan, a healthcare modality records all of that information and the patient's progress and then a clear picture of the effectiveness of the methods emerges. Over time, an effective healthcare modality develops a documented system of verification, analysis, and self-criticism. In this fashion, theory and practices can be revised as needed and kept fresh and vital. If some aspect of theory or practice doesn't work as ascertained by observation and documentation, then that element of theory or practice gets modified. Macrobiotics has not yet evolved to this level. Macrobiotic diagnosis is simple and uncoordinated. There is no way to combine the diagnostic observations of macrobiotics into a diagnosis much more differential or refined than too yang or too yin. That approach can be a place to start, but the refinements and depth of diagnosis necessary for effective treatment are not possible. Macrobiotic theory, no matter how much it is studied, how much it is memorized, or how careful the observations were, cannot provide the specificity and discernment to provide a reliable and effective diagnosis and treatment, especially for complicated conditions. Remember, macrobiotics as Ohsawa taught it was not a healthcare modality. It was moved in that direction by some of his students.

What I saw repeatedly in macrobiotic circles was the trumpeting of a few successes as proof of the effectiveness and the superiority of the macrobiotic system. There was a condescending contempt for Western medicine. Many teachers and many more practitioners avoided going to the doctors, dentists, and other healthcare professionals even for routine exams. Unfortunately, this allowed unhealthy conditions to develop in some, if not many, cases. The prevailing sentiment in macrobiotic circles was that people didn't achieve success with macrobiotics because they were noncompliant. They didn't do as they were told. The unfortunate truth was that too often the victim was blamed for his/her failure.

Macrobiotic theory is inadequate in its scope, diversity, and specificity to make medical diagnoses. Using macrobiotic theory to play doctor does not work.

Most Glaring And Specific Flaw

The application of macrobiotic dietary principles in North

America emphasized a cooling, draining, dispersing, and cleansing energy. That type of dietary practice may provide positive health results for "excess" conditions for a while. With those initial successes someone may become overly attached to the practices that provided success. When his or her condition progresses to where the excess is drained, he or she would likely continue with that draining, cleansing, dispersing, cooling dietary practice. And when positive results are no longer being experienced, many people double down. They pursue an even more draining, more cleansing, more dispersing, more cooling dietary practice. At the same time they are all but unconscious of the fact that they are bingeing on corn chips, Rice Dream, and rice cakes with yinnie's syrup and tahini in the privacy of their own homes out of sight of the macrobiotic "food police."

I have come to recognize that uncontrollable cravings for sweets and fat, no matter how healthy the quality or ingredients of a particular food or recipe, is an early sign of deficiency. When someone develops this kind of deficiency, he or she does not have the tools to turn his or her condition around using macrobiotic theory and practices.

Slavishly adhering to the draining, cleansing, cooling, dispersing diet will eventually create a deficient condition that is readily recognized in TCM as Qi, Blood, Yang or Yin deficiency and in the extreme Essence deficiency. Before going any further, here is a brief introduction to the TCM version of yin and yang and to define some of the TCM terms.

Yin/Yang—TCM Interpretation

I. Origin of Yin and Yang
  A. Taoist "oneness" Unity of the universe, God, Qi
  B. But we perceive dualistically so divide into two—Yin and Yang—earth and heaven
  C. Point of interaction of heaven and earth is Human—makes three
    1. Human holds orderliness between heaven and earth

    2. Human influences and is influenced by heaven
  D. Pure yin and yang do not exist; each contains the seed of the other which makes four entities—the Tai-ji

    1. Greater Yang with
    2. lesser yin
    3. Greater Yin with
    4. lesser yang
  E. Everything is changing—nothing sits still or stays yin or yang, rotation of Tai-ji adds element of time and change and results in the 5 Transformations—the 5 steps of change between yin and yang

II. Yin and Yang—theoretical method for observing and analyzing phenomena
  A. Earliest origin—peasants' observation of alternation of day and night
    1. Light, sun, activity, brightness—yang
    2. Darkness, moon, shade, rest—yin
  B. Yang is the sunny side of the hill, yin is the shady side
  C. Yang symbolizes Heaven (source of heat light and energy) the more immaterial, rarefied, and gas-like state of things—energy; and thus, yang corresponds to creation and activity, expansion and rising
  D. Yin symbolizes Earth, the more dense, cool, material, and solid states of things—matter; and thus, yin corresponds

to condensation and materialization, contraction and descending

Yang–Activation	**Yin–Quiescence**
fire	water
drier	wetter
warm	cool
function	structure
immaterial	material
Qi	blood
produces energy	produces form/matter
expansion	contraction
hollow	solid
aggressive	receptive
rising	descending
above	below
back (exposed)	front (protected)

Qi, Blood, Yin, and Yang Deficiency

Qi deficiency means a lack of function. Whatever job an organ or tissue is supposed to do, it is not doing it well.

Blood deficiency means a lack of moisture in structure. With blood deficiency tissues shrink and dryness is the primary symptom.

Yang deficient means lack of function *and* lack of heat. This pattern is more severe then Qi deficiency because there is lack of function plus cold.

Yin deficient means lack of moisture and structural degeneration. The lack of moisture combined with structural degeneration creates *false* heat. Yin deficiency is a more severe condition than blood deficiency. It is important to know the distinction between true heat and false heat, because false heat is the condition that macrobiotic theory cannot diagnose or treat.

See the diagram on the next page for a graphic representation of these concepts:

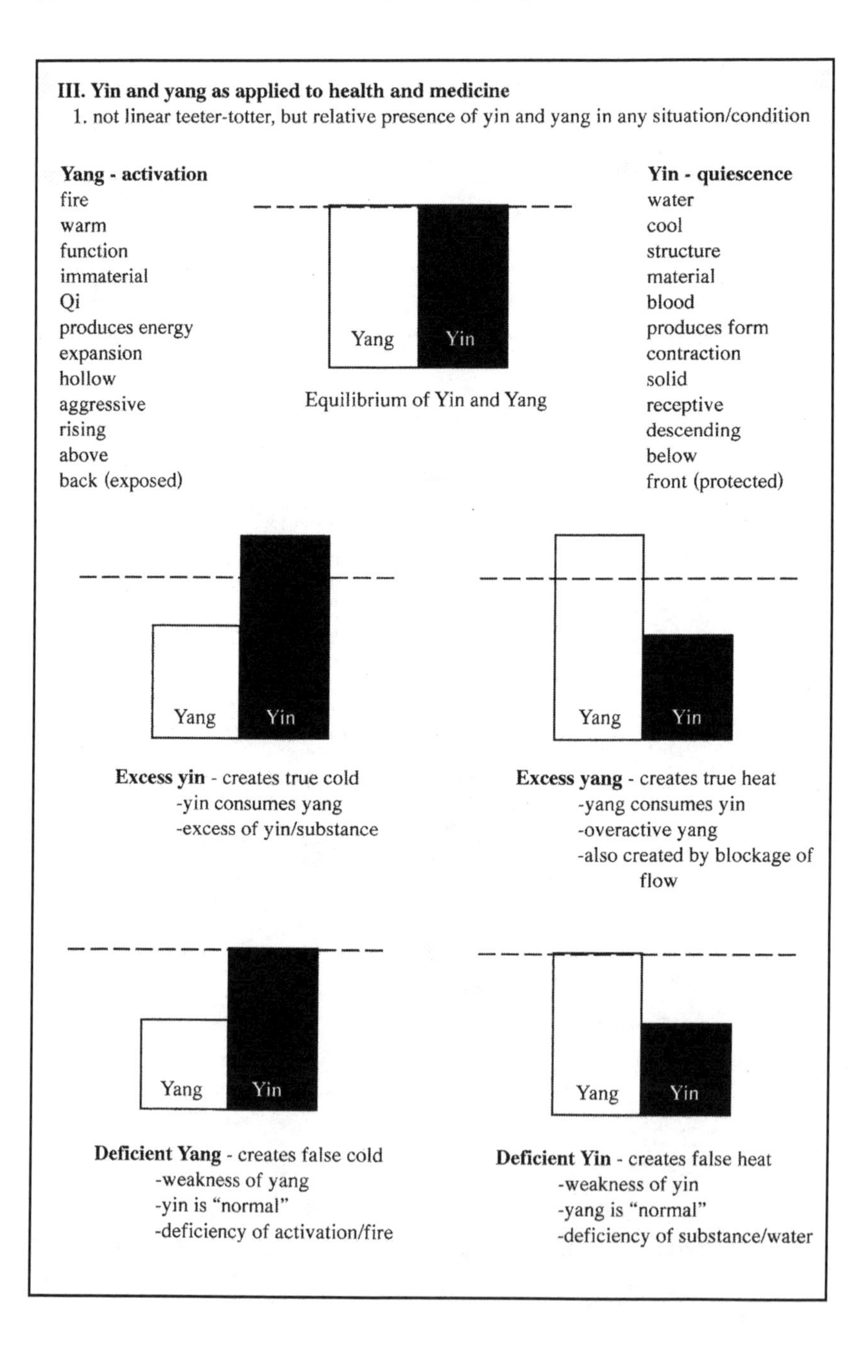
III. Yin and yang as applied to health and medicine
1. not linear teeter-totter, but relative presence of yin and yang in any situation/condition
Yang - activation
fire
warm
function
immaterial
Qi
produces energy
expansion
hollow
aggressive
rising
above
back (exposed)
Yang
Yin
Equilibrium of Yin and Yang
Yin - quiescence
water
cool
structure
material
blood
produces form
contraction
solid
receptive
descending
below
front (protected)
Yang
Yin
Excess yin - creates true cold
-yin consumes yang
-excess of yin/substance
Yang
Yin
Excess yang - creates true heat
-yang consumes yin
-overactive yang
-also created by blockage of flow
Yang
Yin
Deficient Yang - creates false cold
-weakness of yang
-yin is "normal"
-deficiency of activation/fire
Yang
Yin
Deficient Yin - creates false heat
-weakness of yin
-yang is "normal"
-deficiency of substance/water

True heat is an excess condition, too much yang or too much fire energy. An example of true heat is a fever.

False heat (which might look like true heat), on the other hand, is not an excess of yang but rather a deficiency of yin. When yang is "normal" and yin is deficient, the symptoms will look like yang excess relatively speaking, i.e. heat, but the patterns are dramatically different.

A car's radiator cooling system illustrates yin deficiency. An adequate amount of antifreeze or coolant would correspond to the appropriate amount of yin substance in a car's engine, preventing it from overheating. If there is an inadequate amount of coolant (deficient yin), the engine will run hot and possibly overheat. Yin deficiency in humans shows symptoms like dryness in the mouth and throat, dry skin and eyes, hot flashes, night sweats, and a specific type of insomnia.

Insominia—An Illustration

The symptoms of insomnia can illustrate the distinction between excess yang and deficient yin where similar symptoms, here sleep disturbance, could have opposing treatments. If insomnia is due to yang excess, then yang excess generates excess heat. That heat rises and disturbs the heart and the brain disrupting sleep. For insomnia due to yang excess, the cooling, draining, dispersing, cleansing action of the Standard Macrobiotic Diet would likely be helpful.

If insomnia is due to yin deficiency, then the depleted substance of yin deficiency is unable to restrain normal yang. So here too, the ascending yang disturbs the heart and brain disrupting sleep. Sleep is disrupted in both conditions but the diagnosis and treatment is different. For yin deficient sleep patterns, the cooling, draining, dispersing, cleansing action of the Standard Macrobiotic Diet would likely aggravate the condition because it would further deplete the substance (yin) of the body. For yin deficiency sleep patterns, one's condition needs to be built up, not drained or dispersed.

An Early Sign of Deficiency

The craving for sweets and fats is a survival response. Physiologically speaking, the body's prime directive is to supply glucose to the brain for its functions. Brain activity is the definition of life. When someone has been on a diet of inadequate nutrition long enough, a primitive drive for survival takes over. I imagine that the primitive drive is to supply glucose to the brain at any cost.

The quickest way to supply glucose to the brain in terms of food is to take simple sugars into the mouth where they are absorbed directly through the tissues and go directly into the bloodstream. Once in the bloodstream those simple sugars (glucose) are transported the short distance to the brain and the prime directive is temporarily fulfilled. Life has been preserved.

From the chin up we are happy; from the chin down imbalances ensue. This primitive drive is so strong that no matter how resolute, how well schooled, how strenuous the efforts at self-control, the primitive drive prevails. In macrobiotic circles these primitive drives run rampant in private moments and are excused as festive occasions in public. In many cases the deprivation is so profound that it leads too serious bingeing, to the point of making one's stomach hurt. I know because I have been there.

Essence Deficiency

Beyond the deficiencies of Qi, Blood, Yin, and Yang, is Essence deficiency. Early on in my association with macrobiotics I noticed a pattern of poor dental health among long-time macrobiotic practitioners. Even that very first book, *Zen Macrobiotics*, with the photo of George Ohsawa on the back cover caught my attention. I had lived in Japan for several years and noticed the state of dental health in the general population. At the time I lived there, late 1970s, it seemed as though baby teeth were thought to be expendable. Children typically had dark spots on their teeth and they appeared to be allowed to decay without attention. Many adults had crumbling teeth, or as in the Ohsawa photo on the back of *Zen Macrobiotics*, gold margin restorations. I passed it off at the time as the state of dental technology and the societal view of dental hygiene practices. But now, I believe there was more to it, at least in the macrobiotic community. First let me describe the TCM notion of Essence and Essence deficiency.

Essence (or Jing) is defined in TCM as the body's potential. Essence is the origin of constitutional strength, is in charge of growth and development, produces bone marrow, and is stored and controlled by the kidneys. Pre-natal Essence is inherited from ancestors and is a fixed amount. Post-natal Essence can be created by our life choices. Ideally, Essence is depleted to the benefit and nourishment of the spirit. It is thought that if one's life has spiritual development, that the decline of the physical due to Essence consumption is accompanied/compensated by a deeper appreciation of life and its spiritual dimension. Nevertheless, when Essence is expended we die.

The depletion of Essence comes from trauma, injury, bearing children, producing physical energy in general, ejaculating too frequently, and from taking stimulants that do not provide any nourishment. Caffeine is one of those stimulants. Other drugs like cocaine, amphetamine, methamphetamine, and methylpheridate (commonly known as Ritalin) deplete Essence even more seriously. It should be added that insufficient rest, poor diet, stress, over-work, and over-thinking (worry) can strain the body's replaceable resources of Qi, Yin, and Blood to the point that Essence is consumed to "keep going."

Essence is like money in the bank. The kidneys release some Essence and that potential energy is converted into functional energy. Caffeine and other stimulants are capable of stimulating the kidneys to release Essence without providing any nourishment (think of making a withdrawal from your savings account without making any deposit). Caffeine is not bad, but it is a medicinal quality substance, i.e., it is fast-acting, narrowly focused, and dramatic in its effect. If someone is hovering on the brink of a more serious condition, caffeine might provide a temporary boost (at a cost of expended Essence) to avoid developing a more serious condition. As a medicine, caffeine can have a positive effect. However, prolonged, regular, and excessive ingestion of caffeine will deplete Essence.

Essence depletion proceeds naturally with age as a small amount of Essence is needed each day for normal life functions. Many of the symptoms of Essence deficiency look like the accepted, but not natural, signs of aging; slowing down, lower back pain, knee pain, sexual dysfunction (including erectile dysfunction, low/no libido, premature ejaculation, infertility, and impotence), and a host of chronic, inflammatory, and immunological disorders. And since in TCM theory, the kidneys rule the bones and teeth, osteoporosis and poor dental health are thought to result from Essence depletion.

It is poor dental health that I noticed in virtually all of the Japanese teachers who came to the United States and in Ohsawa. Some American teachers and counselors had or developed poor dental health as well. Some of that poor dental health may have been due to the level of dental care and hygiene, but I feel it also could have been, at least in part, from pursuing a dietary and lifestyle pattern that was so cleansing, dispersing, draining, and cooling that Qi, Yin, and Blood became so deficient that Essence was tapped to survive.

Personal Experience

About ten years into my personal interpretation of a dedicated macrobiotic diet and lifestyle practice, I developed the need for two root canals and gum surgery. This is totally anecdotal, but after the "bacon incident" and awakening to the need to conserve and cultivate Essence, I have not had any serious dental or gum issues these past 20 years. Anecdotal as it is, to my observation there is a noticeable pattern of Essence depletion among long-time macrobiotic practitioners.

Essence depletion is the most extreme deficiency and usually doesn't occur for many years, but the consistent pattern of Essence deficiency I have observed in the macrobiotic community leads me to believe that the macrobiotic dietary and lifestyle practices in vogue from the 1960s to present play a significant role.

Summary

Summing up, using macrobiotic theoretical principles to diagnose and treat health conditions will have mixed results. The application of macrobiotic theory and practices to address excess conditions may result in some improvement of that condition. However, for deficiency conditions, particularly yin and essence deficiency, attempting to diagnose and treat them with macrobiotic theory and practices may aggravate, rather than improve someone's condition. Macrobiotics is not a medical modality.

Chapter 5

Nourishing the Yin

The theoretical formations of yin and yang are skewed in favor of yang masculine energy. The macrobiotic version of yin/yang characterizes yang as more active, positive, and materially oriented. The macrobiotic theoretical characterizations of yin are more inactive, negative, and spiritually oriented. On a larger scale, I feel that yang active-heat-fire-competitive-masculine energy has dominated across many energetic dimensions on our planet for at least the last 200 years.

The Industrial Revolution

The advent of the Industrial Revolution closely parallels the extraction and utilization of fossil fuels, petroleum products in particular. As a civilization, we have increasingly extracted nonrenewable resources such as coal, petroleum, and many other minerals essential for the building of civilization as we know it. Use of these resources has greatly expanded human potential. Look around at a modern city, particularly one in a northern climate like New York, Chicago, London, Paris, or Moscow. Skyscrapers pierce the landscape, roads and rails hum with the transportation of people and commodities. Moreover, these activities continue virtually uninterrupted, regardless of weather and climate conditions. All of this is largely made possible by the exploitation of nonrenewable natural resources like coal and petroleum. These resources heat our homes and offices, bring light to the darkness making around the clock activity possible, and enable us to move rapidly from place to place, whether it's across town or between continents. The dominant consequence of exploiting nonrenewable fossil fuels is to generate heat and light. In the TCM sense of yin/yang, these nonrenewable fossil fuels are the yin quality of the earth's crust. They are deep, dark, cool concentrations of biomass energy created over billions of years. The length of time for them to be created is itself a yin characteristic.

What have we done with these resources? We have extracted them from the earth and burned or exploded them to generate heat and light to build and power civilization. Heat and light enable more activity and more intensity of activity. Heat and light are both yang characteristics.

As a civilization, we will have consumed the majority of these nonrenewable fossil fuels in a scant 200 to 300 years. That is the nature of yang, to consume fuel and create heat, light, and movement at a steeply disproportionate rate at which these resources can be created or replaced. It is my assessment that our planet has had its yin quality depleted of all things contained in and on it. Planet earth is yin deficient. To save our planet and ourselves, to heal our planet and ourselves, I feel it is urgent to nourish yin across-the-board, from the planetary to the personal level and to the cellular and microscopic levels.

The predominant and now almost ubiquitous effect of yin depletion on human health and lifestyle is burn-out. The yin is consumed, all burnt up if you will, in one's personal body and civilization. We, as individuals, as a civilization, and as a planet, are on the edge of exhaustion and collapse.

Work Hard, Play Hard

Another aspect of the Industrial Revolution is that competition, or an awareness of competition and threats to success, resulted in aggressive actions and business practices to succeed or remain in power or control.

Personally, we consume our yin, deplete our reserves, and predictably turn to stimulants like caffeine, nicotine, and drugs to keep going. Rest and relaxation time has become less and less. More of our time is not only devoted to working hard, but also to playing hard as well. The dominant energy is to be active and consuming of yin. We don't take breaks. We don't address that afternoon slump with a nap. We work through our lunch hour. We take work home on evenings and weekends. The competitive urge to get and stay ahead dominates. We are unable (or choose not) to replace the yin that has been consumed.

Consumption of yin is especially hard on women. Depletion of yin in females can have a direct impact on fertility. The exhaustion of yin, the reserve of substances (especially Blood, part of yin in the TCM concept of yin/yang), deprives a woman of the requisite substance and energy to conceive, carry to term, and breastfeed a child. I've heard many stories from patients about layoffs and downsizing with the result that one person has to do the work of two or three people. We have more pressure and stress, always surrounded by noise and energetic violence, whether it's fighting traffic, elbowing our way onto the subway, or trying to move around what we think is a slow moving car or a slow walking person. Then, there are the kids in the household to manage and care for as well. We have to stay up late to get everything done. Still all revved up, we can't unwind in the evening without a drink or two or three and very likely then don't get enough sleep, which often leads to taking a sleep aid like Ambien or Lunesta. All the while, there is less and less time to shop, cook, and eat in a peaceful environment. And then the next day, we to do it all over again.

Overcommitted, we are pulled in many directions at once. Add in money issues like a mortgage, credit card debt, and money for the kids' soccer shoes and saving for their college and we can feel like we're right on the edge of losing it. Heaven forbid there should be a sudden dramatic reversal or interruption in this breakneck pace of life. One can lose his or her job. One's spouse, kids, or parents can develop a serious health issue. A natural disaster can strike. It can look pretty grim. An individual, or any system, can only stand a certain amount of stress or pressure. When tolerance for pressure is exceeded, the system collapses. This collapse is the physical manifestation of severely depleted yin. There is no longer any fuel (yin) and the individual's or system's yang energy with its forceful aggressiveness now comes crashing down like a fuel-spent rocket falling back to earth. When yin is exhausted, a system, or someone's individual health, will collapse. Think of the recent bubbles, whether high-tech, housing, or finance. They all have in common this exhaustion of yin and eventual collapse. This is where civilization is headed given our current consumption patterns. On a personal level, it's the chronic, degenerative, and wasting illnesses like chronic fatigue, diabetes, cancer and heart disease (which are all avoidable).

An Irony

Yin feminine energy from the micro to the macro scale is being consumed and depleted to support the masculine need for fuel. Without the cooling and lubricating substance of yin, an individual or a larger system generates friction and heat. This friction and heat can take the shape of abrasive disagreements in personal relationships or between nations in the form of war. This has always been the case on our planet, but it seems like these days there are armed conflicts and wars going on in so many places. War is a clear metaphor for yang consuming yin. War consumes the blood and treasure of a society—even the so-called winning side is depleted. War produces no nourishment to replace the yin that was consumed. It is ironic that a number of the current world armed conflicts are taking place in oil-rich locations and that war (yang) is raging over possession and exploitation of yin-rich oil. To influence and change this pattern of yang consumption of yin, we can all do something very influential. We can attend to our own personal yin depletion, pursue practices that nourish our yin, and eventually create more balance between yin and yang.

Nourishing the Yin—General Practices

Here are some general ideas and practices that nourish yin followed by advice for general and specific organ systems.

- create peace and quiet in your life even if it's just for a few minutes a day.
- take regular breaks throughout the day.
- take afternoon naps when possible.
- cultivate regularity and rhythm in your lifestyle habits, e.g., regular mealtimes, bedtime and waking time, exercise, and social interaction.
- it is absolutely crucial to get enough rest and sleep so you don't have to resort to caffeine, nicotine, and other stimulants. Rest can't be negotiated.
- seek wide open spaces, panoramic views, and horizon gazing, especially if you do close work like on a computer all day.
- work at understanding your limitations (physically, mentally, emotionally) so you don't burnout. As Herman Aihara would say, if you respect your limitations you can experience freedom. Burn out is a kind of prison, you become a slave to the symptoms of burnout.
- don't take on the problems of the world. Do what needs to be done in your immediate circumstance.
- ask for help, pray, meditate, and reflect both practically and divinely.
- whatever the cost in time and money, cook your meals at the household level. This is one of the fundamental community building activities. Nourish the social circle in your home.
- have fun! Be sincere but not overly serious. Find levity wherever you can.
- breathe! Breath is the primary means of energy acquisition. It's always available, it's always calming, and it always unblocks stuck energy.
- don't over commit, learn to say no when you feel over extended.
- learn to trust—this will reduce worry and anxiety.
- cultivate self-confidence; whatever the challenge, you can find a way forward.

- learn to recognize negative destructive thoughts and patterns and just don't go there.
- express gratitude. Gratitude heals the heart. First thing in the morning and the last thing at night be grateful for all of the blessings that you enjoy.

Nourishing the Yin—Organ Systems Signs/Symptoms

Yin organs: LV (liver), SP (spleen), LU (lung), HT (heart), KD (kidney)—are the primary focus. They all:

- manufacture and store Qi, Blood, body fluids
- are continuously functioning
- are vital as one can't live without them
- are protected by bone

Yang Organs: GB (gall bladder), SI (small intestine), ST (stomach), LI (large intestine), BL (urinary bladder). These organs:

- receive/digest food; transmit and excrete waste
- function intermittently
- are not protected by bone
- can be removed and a person can still live
- are protected by muscle

Nourishing the Yin Organs Specifically

1. Liver—"The General of the Body"

Functions—stores blood; spreads Qi; nourishes tendons/ligaments, eyes, and menstruation.

Impacted by—emotions (constraint): hot spicy food; alcohol; greasy foods; staying up late; overuse of eyes such as too much reading, watching TV, and staring at screens especially late at night; blood loss; birth; trauma.

Liver Blood Deficiency—contracting dried up tendons, dry eyes, weak vision, scanty menses with prolonged interval.

Liver Yin Deficiency—tissues break down and heat occurs; dry and inflamed eyes.

Liver Qi Stagnation—pain or discomfort anywhere along the sides of the body, depression, mood swings, sighing, hiccups, frustration, inappropriate anger, sensation of a lump in the throat. The experience of wanting to do, say, or become anything and feeling blocked.

Menses—less than 28 days is due to Qi Deficiency or Heat in the Blood; more than 28 days is due to Blood Deficiency, Blood Stagnation, or Yang Deficiency (cold); Irregular menses is due to LV Qi Stagnation, LV Blood Deficiency, or SP Deficiency.

Nourishing the Liver

• Chlorophyll-rich foods such as leafy greens plus mung bean sprouts, cucumber, tofu, millet, sea vegetables, watercress, flax, borage, black currant, primrose oils, animal liver, dark grapes, raspberries.

• Sour taste - plum (ume extract), lemon; sour astringes and will keep fluids in and move Qi upwards—this helps to retain yin substance

• Address emotional stuck spots, frustration, and learn how to change.

• Dance, yoga, gardening (full of wood/spring/liver energy).

• Twisting exercises such as golf with an undulating green landscape, twisting swing, and percussive smack of a little ball that relieves constraint.

• Gaze at the horizon, especially green landscapes to get the big picture; breathe; be creative; rest; chew well; establish appropriate boundaries.

• Be asleep before 11:00 p.m. (beginning of wood liver/ gallbladder time of day) so you can get deep sleep during liver time (1:00 to 3:00 a.m.). This is when the liver stores blood, which conserves yin substance.

2. Spleen—"The Earth"

Functions—Mother Earth - almost pure function, doesn't store much; transforms and transports food, information, and experience;

controls digestion; rules the limbs and the flesh; lifts up and prevents collapse/prolapse; holds together/maintains integrity of structure; rules concentration, memory, and worrying.

Impacted by—cold, damp, irregular diet or over eating, "dirty" food, spoiled food, cold/raw foods, over-thinking (worry/anxiety), too much sweet food.

Spleen Qi Deficiency—bruise easily, prolapse of structure (uterus, pelvic floor muscles, falling arches), diarrhea, no appetite, any organ or structure not doing any of its functions, creates mucus/phlegm, inability to see options in decision making.

Spleen Yang Deficiency—Spleen Qi Deficiency plus cold.

Supporting the Spleen

• Be a mother to yourself first, so you can share mother energy with the rest of the world.

• Cultivate sweet relationships and times so you don't dive into eating heavy sweets to counter your natural yearning for sweet.

• Adapt to change—physical, emotional, mental, spiritual, beliefs.

• Take frequent breaks from mental work and computer/device screens.

• Eat easily digested, yet luscious foods like soups, stews, porridges, gravies, rich baked beans; deep sweet squash, sweet potatoes, carrots, parsnips, pumpkin, garbanzo beans, onions, scallions, leeks, ginger (dried for better digestion), cinnamon, garlic, nutmeg, bone stock soups, ghee.

• Eat meals in an harmonious environment; digestion occurs best when the body/mind is in parasympathetic mode.

• Avoid heavy oily foods, too many nuts, fried food, dairy, sugar, anything that strains digestion, excessive raw foods, large meals, eating late at night.

3. Lungs—"The Tender Organ"

Functions—controls skin, pores, and body hair; interface between inner/outer environments via breath and skin; protects surface from external pathogens; controls respiration; controls nose and sinuses. Lungs are the primary means of acquiring Qi energy—"Master of Qi"—mixes air Qi with food Qi from the spleen to create blood. Lungs are animal spirit.

Impacted by—wind, dirty air, dust, pollution, external pathogens, shallow or poor breathing techniques, excessive/strained talking, smoking, grief/sadness, weakened by lying down too much, weakened by too much/little touching (skin).

LU Qi Deficiency—shortness of breath, breathing through the mouth, quiet speech, catches cold easily, weak pulse, fatigue, allergies, asthma (tissue looks okay, but does not function), Kidney not grasping Lung Qi.

LU Yin Deficiency—structural: irritation, dry, hacking cough, emphysema.

LU Phelgm accumulation—from SP Deficiency, phlegm builds up in lungs.

Healing the Lungs

- Get enough rest, take breaks, rest voice, practice good posture, breathe deeply.
- Eat onion, garlic, turnip, ginger, horseradish, cabbage, daikon, sea vegetables like kombu and wakame, flaxseed, beta carotene foods to protect mucus and surface membranes, carrots, winter squash, pumpkin, broccoli, parsley, kale, mustard greens (chlorophyll discharges chemical residues), fiber foods such as whole grains and vegetables.
- Reduce/eliminate dairy; use goat milk products with cinnamon if desired.
- Eat baked pear and apple with cinnamon.
- Eliminate sticky emotional attachments; fully grieve; find closure to emotional pain/trauma; know when and how to move on when relationships dissolve.
- Practice appropriate and satisfying touching.

4. Heart—"The Emperor"

Functions—Circulation of Blood; houses shen (shen is the capacity of the mind to form ideas and is the desire of the personality to live life. When shen is weak an individual's eyes may lack luster and his or her thinking/speech may be muddled); sends, receives and holds emotions; rules the complexion.

Impacted by emotions—true emotions (bodily expression without lingering), especially joy and enthusiasm enhance immune system; false emotions (aftermath, add on, detached from situation, attachment beyond utility) deplete. Non-joyful thoughts and people as well as over-joyful, over-excitement deplete heart energy. Emotional stress usually does not affected heart directly—any/all conditions from other organs are passed on to heart; every syndrome of heart affects rhythms; heart can have all conditions. Going through life at top speed. Bitter taste—firming, tonifying.

HT Qi Deficiency—(weak, slow pulse) weak circulation, slow or weak in body/fatigue, dull witted (shen Deficiency).

HT Blood Deficiency—restless thinking, flitting, straying mental focus, insomnia, poor memory.

HT Yin Deficiency—hyper mentally, frazzled, excess/no laughter, emotionally exhausted.

HT Yang Deficiency—weak circulation and coldness, facial pallor, depression.

Healing the Heart: Strengthen/Balance Other Organs

- Improved awareness of speech will strengthen the heart, reins in a scattered mind.
- Practice prayer, meditation/reflection, singing, chanting, speaking (up), getting in touch with one's personal heartfelt truth, light heartedness, have fun.
- Eat whole grains like brown rice, oats, and whole wheat (spelt, kamut); slight bitter taste as in olives and leafy greens; mushrooms, especially reishi.
- Eat silicon foods such as barley, oat porridge, cucumber, celery, lettuce.

• Eat fruits like mulberries, lemons, Schisandra berry that calm the mind.

• Use dill, basil, chamomile, rose hips.

• Use goat milk and ghee if desired.

5. Kidneys—"Body's Battery Pack/Power Station, "Reserve Tank"

Function—Filters/reabsorbs/eliminates electrolytes, glucose, proteins, fluid (urine); urinary function; rules growth and development of bone health, hearing, head hair; seat of excessive fear/insecurity; supplies both yin and yang energy.

Impacted by—overwork, excess sexuality (men—too frequent seminal emissions; women—too many or too close pregnancies/births); depleted by disease of any other organs because kidneys use reserves to combat any weakness or challenge to health. Standing for long periods of time strains the kidneys.

KD Qi Deficiency—general weakness, low back/knee pain or weakness, tired/fatigue, no sex drive, can't hold on to things, urine leakage, frequent urination, sperm leakage.

KD Yang Deficiency—KD Qi Deficiency plus cold.

KD Yin Deficiency—hot, restless, dried out, can't sleep; aging and degenerations of physical body; menopause—everything dries, often has back pain.

Healing the Kidneys

Practices to Strengthen Kidneys:

• Regulate salt intake and use sea salt rather than commercial salt. Cook salt into food, don't add at the table. Salt needs are individual. If something tastes salty it is too salty. If something tastes bland it is not salty enough.

• Avoid dry, hard, crispy (salty) snack foods like chips, crackers, popcorn, and too much bread. (Stomach must turn all food into soup.)

• Walk—especially outdoors and uphill, walk barefoot on morning dew.

• Breathe fresh air.

• Do something to sweat like vigorous work (gardening/house cleaning), aerobic exercise, or sauna.

• Take warm baths with salt or bath minerals.

• Practice core strengthening/trunk rotating exercises such as Pilates, yoga, Tai Chi, Qi Gong.

• Massage (rub Tiger Balm into) the kidney source point on the sole of the foot.

• Rest/nap in the late afternoon (3:00 to 5:00 p.m.).

• Avoid caffeine and refined sugar.

• Apply ginger compress (or hot water bottle or heating pad) over mid/low back.

• Attend to dental hygiene—brush, floss, oil pull (swish ½ teaspoon organic coconut oil in your mouth for 15 minutes every morning first thing), regular check ups with a dentist.

Diet to Strengthen Kidneys:

• Nourish KD Yin: millet, barley, tofu, string beans, black beans, mung beans, kidney beans, kuzu, watermelon, wheat germ, sea vegetables. Small amounts of eggs, pork, cheese (goat).

• Avoid coffee, tobacco, alcohol.

• Nourish KD Yang—stoke digestive fire with bone stock soups, cinnamon, walnuts, onion family, ginger, clove, fennel, black pepper. Avoid cooling raw foods, excess salt.

• Tonify KD Qi—parsley, sweet brown rice, wheat berries (sourdough bread).

Chapter 6

Balancing Yin and Yang

Since its inception, macrobiotic yin/yang theory has favored yang energy; and, it is my view that yang energy continues to dominate in macrobiotic theory and practice. I feel this is largely due to the formulation of yin and yang (favoring yang) and to the influence of masculine, male, yang energy in macrobiotic theory, teaching, counseling, and practice. In this sense, to restore balance it is necessary to nourish yin; i.e. to decrease the dominance of yang. However, to nourish yin is only half of the job.

Just as over-emphasis on yang can create imbalances, overemphasis on yin also can create imbalances. The ongoing and ever-present challenge is to balance yin and yang. It is a dynamic interplay between two energetic forces, not the dominance of one or the other. Yang energy is necessary and vital to maintaining balance, just as yin energy is necessary and vital to maintain balance. All the while we are nourishing yin, we must remain mindful that yang also has an equal part to play.

Good Judgment

The solution to balancing yin and yang lies in mindfulness, clear thinking, and good judgment. These qualities enable us to understand the dynamics of change, the subtle interplay of yin and yang. Then we are able to make an appropriate choice to restore balance to a situation, relationship, or condition of health that is trending too far in one direction. These are the "magic spectacles" (Ohsawa's term) that allow us to see behind and in front of events. We can determine the choices that enable us to avoid the extremes of disharmony such as injury, illness, disease, and collapse of our own bodies or of a larger system. Truly we must develop these thinking and judgment skills for ourselves. A teacher or a counselor is not always there to make choices for us. And indeed, if we understand the truth of our being and clearly pursue that, no one outside of ourselves can ever make a better choice for us than we can make on our own. Each of us is privy to the inner workings of our own heart, mind, and soul. Everyone and everything else is at best secondhand.

Remember, yin and yang do not really exist as discrete entities. Their only meaning is in a relative sense; i.e., something is designated as yin in relation to something else. Another way to think of yin and yang is as a metaphor for energy transformation. One observable constant in the universe is change. Ancient cultures, indeed all cultures, strive to find ways to describe the dynamics of change and to develop a reliable system of interpretation to reduce unpredictability and adverse outcomes in the experience of life. By reliable system, I mean a system of energetic concepts that, when mindfully applied, can produce an interpretation of a proposition, condition, or circumstance that yields a fairly accurate prediction of a physical outcome. This interpretation is one of the functions of yin and yang.

Oneness

The unification of yin and yang is the Tao, Oneness, the Whole. Yet, Oneness also is not a specific object but rather an energetic state, or state of being. The balance of yin and yang is a metaphor for how we can live in a sustaining manner, maintaining balance so that larger planetary, social, economic, and physical systems, as well as our personal health, do not collapse.

Indeed conceptually, yin and yang will always "balance" over long periods of time with fluctuations and swings in between. That is how the Universe continues to exist. On a personal level, we attempt to understand the dynamics of yin and yang to be able to influence the outcome of events on a shorter time frame, say, for the purpose of influencing our personal health.

I believe we must examine our deepest beliefs around yin and yang and masculine and feminine. Many biases and imbalances have been coded into our thinking and action. For example, it is often thought that it is more blessed to give than take, that it is more spiritual to give selflessly. This can lead to an imbalance. As we have seen in the depletion of yin, it is possible to give so much away that one makes oneself sick. That is neither balanced nor is it spiritual. The balance of yin and yang is equally giving (feminine) and taking (masculine). The practice of Tai Qi is the cultivation of balancing yin and yang, the feminine and masculine, the receptive and the aggressive, and the seamless and spontaneous interplay of these two symbols of energetic states. Tai Qi improves balance and coordination, strengthens the internal circulation of Qi, and trains us to move our energies to influence and transform circumstances. Tai Qi also helps us to harmonize and find unity even in separation, to explore our limits, and to recognize when we can go further and when we need to retreat.

Integration

Another way to think of the balance of yin and yang is integration, the reconciliation of these two opposing forces in ourselves, to become a fully functioning integrated and harmonized human being. We learn to enjoy the transition phases when we switch (figuratively speaking) from feminine to masculine or masculine to feminine to suit the needs of the situation, like waves pushing water onto the beach and pulling water back into the sea. The transition is so smooth that there is no moment at which the energy of transformation is exclusively forceful or yielding. In one energy or action there is always the seed of an opposing energy or action. Just as waves swirl and mix a bit before going out or coming back in, we can begin to feel within ourselves, during the transition of shifting from one to the other, that internal Qi mixing and swirling as intention is redirected. The challenge is directing life force in one direction and then in the other as needed to maintain or restore health.

The dynamic and ongoing balance of yin and yang is a wonderful metaphor for how well an individual can survive an extreme moment in life, just prior to becoming its opposite. To survive an extreme moment requires faith that everything does change, faith that there is a natural order, faith that the extreme will be transformed, and faith that balance will return. What bolsters one's faith is a knowledge of the dynamics of change and the application of yin and yang theory. We do not have to be victims willy-nilly of the dynamics of change. Through one's study and experimentation with the concepts of yin and yang and the dynamics of change, one can reliably influence the outcome of events or influence current circumstances and, in effect, help create one's reality. To move gracefully and effectively between feminine and masculine, between yin and yang, we must get beyond our familial, social, and sexual conditioning. We have to peel away the layers of encrusted imbalances to get in touch with the innate sense of equilibrium that we all have. Cultivating intuition is very helpful for getting in touch with one's innate sense of equilibrium. We can open up an experiment with the less developed aspect of our being (be it feminine or masculine), making it stronger so that wholeness can be achieved.

A relationship is an entity distinct from the features of the individuals involved in the relationship. A relationship has its own nature, its own state of health, its own equilibrium. An unbalanced relationship in which the individuals are not whole makes for an unhealthy relationship. Often this state of imbalance manifests as symptoms in only one of the partners but, likely, it is the relationship that is dysfunctional.

Polarized

It seems to be an unaffordable luxury these days to be strongly polarized. Witness the gridlock in Congress. Because our primary institutions are less supportive of our relationships and sense of community, and because we are increasingly on our own, we need to learn to get along with each other on our own in order to maintain friendships and families, jobs and communities. These times can lead to synthesis, integration, cooperation, and sharing. Humans were not meant to be alone; we are very social creatures. To get along, to avoid conflicts and isolation, we must tone down our over-yang competitiveness and boost our yin, compassionate, empathetic energies. In any relationship, acknowledging another's strengths and even encouraging the development of another's strengths is strongly beneficial. If one can take full advantage of complementarity, then one is able to switch from yang to yin, masculine to feminine, quickly, spontaneously, and gracefully—being the supporter in one moment, being supported in the next. We can view relationships as a collective whole, acknowledge our integration and connectedness from individuals to planet-wide, and beyond. We can learn to work fluidly and effortlessly between the opposing and complementary forces of yin and yang, feminine and masculine. Study the theory that makes sense to you be it macrobiotics, TCM, Ayurveda, Shamanism, Western medicine, or any and all of the great religions and philosophical traditions. Every way of thinking illuminates some pieces of the puzzle of existence. No one system exhaustively knows or can explain everything. I don't know of a more spiritual or effective way to balance yin and yang than to pay careful, close attention to the details of daily life. The basics: healthy diet by way of mindful shopping, cooking, chewing, and cleaning; appropriate exercise; adequate rest; creating a peaceful and harmonious environment; managing and transforming stress; maintaining healthy emotional relationships; fulfilling work; and a loving heart.

Part 2

A Macrobiotic Diet

Chapter 7

One of the Great Cuisines of the World

Importance of Daily Life

Macrobiotic theory emphasizes the importance of diet and lifestyle. Many philosophies and theories of living have no mention of diet and lifestyle while others pay lip service, but macrobiotics places great importance on daily living and the many decisions we make each day regarding diet, exercise, food choices, cooking, and rest. Indeed, these practices form the foundation of a macrobiotic lifestyle.

George Ohsawa's concept of freedom stems from understanding limitation in the areas of diet, exercise, and other activities. It suggests that unless we pay attention to these aspects of life we are continually imprisoned by compensating for our excesses and deficiencies. To build a firm foundation of health through daily lifestyle practices is a profound insight contributing to experiencing a fulfilling life.

Naturally then, it follows that macrobiotic theory emphasizes quality of life. In our fast-paced-profits-at-all-costs-media-saturated society, support for quality of life is hard to come by. Macrobiotic thinking supports taking the time to prepare healthy meals, to exercise sensibly, to spend time with family and friends, and to commune with nature. This feature of macrobiotics is a healing balm, a welcome antidote to the crush of modern life. Anyone who has been to a macrobiotic summer camp can testify to the validity of this idea.

Principal Food

One of George Ohsawa's ideas that has become ever more relevant today is the idea of "principal food." A principal food is one that can be cultivated in harmony with the resources of our planet (i.e. sustainable) and can feed the entire population of the world. Animal-sourced food does not qualify as a principal food. The excesses and abuses of animal-based food production are well known. The resources and expense required to produce animal-based foods limits or precludes their availability to many people of the world.

Ohsawa advanced complex carbohydrates—whole grains—as a principal food. In combination with secondary foods such as cooked and some raw vegetables, soups (miso), sea vegetables, some fruits, and small amounts of animal food, if needed, the whole world can be feed without destroying our living environment.

Society in general may not yet acknowledge it, but in no small way, Ohsawa's idea of principal food presents a strategy for humans to avoid famine and potential extinction. This is a major contribution to civilization.

The shape and arrangement of human teeth as an indicator of how humans have eaten over many years is an idea I first encountered through macrobiotics. "The 32 teeth include 20 molars and premolars for grinding grains, legumes, and seeds; eight incisors for cutting vegetables; and four canines for tearing animal and seafood. Expressed as a ratio of teeth designed for grain use, for vegetable use, and for animal use, the proportion comes to 5:2:1; and of all vegetable quality to animal quality, 7:1." *The Book of Macrobiotics*, Michio Kushi, p. 78.

Ohsawa did not emphasize animal foods, but neither did he absolutely prohibit them. I would love to see a civilization of humans thriving on a plant-based diet and I do believe that it is possible, even necessary, if we are to survive as a species. However, there are a few essential intermediate steps in achieving that state.

First, we must improve the quality of the soil used for farming so that foods cultivated have the necessary vitality and nutrition to fully nourish us. Second, each of us must take it upon ourselves to strengthen our digestion so that we can assimilate the nutrients in the plant-based foods that we consume. Third, many people are so weak and/or sick, not just as individuals but as whole communities, that animal-based foods may be required to restore strength and vitality…as a bridge, not as a permanent dependence.

Furthermore, Traditional Chinese Medicine (TCM) teaches that the primary means of acquiring energy is through the breath. As such, air quality becomes an essential component for overall nourishment and energy acquisition. Personally, I experience a noticeable difference in vitality and well-being when I am above 5000 feet, at the seashore, or on an island. In those areas, the air quality is generally much better than in large cities. Current photos of Chinese cities show a choking amount of air pollution and smog. Cleaning up the air we breathe is an essential component to sustaining human life on planet earth.

Ohsawa repeatedly emphasized that freedom and independence from addictions is possible through a macrobiotic diet and lifestyle. Currently, excess animal-based foods and processed/refined foods such as sugar are our culturally sanctioned food addictions. Fossil fuels are our energy addiction. These addictions are killing us. These consumption patterns must change if we are to survive.

Cooking Techniques

The cooking knowledge and skills that are available through the study of macrobiotics are unsurpassed among all the great cuisines of the world. Nowhere else does a theory match climate, locale, age, activity level, and a myriad of other personal characteristics so appropriately to foods and cooking styles. This is truly an empowering quality of macrobiotics. Here are the ideas that we should eat warming foods in winter, cooling foods in summer, and more warming foods in Minnesota than in Florida; that more active people need stronger nutrition or greater volume than less active people; that older folks maybe should eat less than younger people; and especially, people with serious health concerns should eat according to their condition.

The concept of a dialectic (yin/yang) is one of the most useful ideas in macrobiotic theory. The use of yin and yang gives macrobiotics a powerful tool for matching food choices and cooking styles to the needs of an individual. And truly, each of us is a unique individual, as unique as our fingerprints. Ancestry, age, gender, activity level, personality, mood, and environmental factors such as location, climate, season, and locally available foods are just a few of the characteristics that differentiate each of us one from another. To optimally nourish ourselves, all of the features that make us unique should be taken into account when deciding what foods to cook and what cooking styles to use.

Using the macrobiotic dialectic combined with macrobiotic food preparation techniques, it is possible to stabilize one's physiology. George Ohsawa thought that freedom could be achieved by respect for our limitations. Ohsawa believed that if one understands one's limitations, that is, what type and quantity of food is sufficient at a meal, and stays within that limitation, then infinite freedom is possible.

By respecting one's limitations and not straying outward to excess or retreating inward to deficiency, the overall system (health, physiology) does not have to expend excessive energy to maintain a state of physical health. If one is consistently exceeding one's limitations, the system has to divert precious energy to restore health. In this fashion we become a slave to our imbalances. Precious energy that could be used for creative activity (realizing one's dream) has to be diverted to restoring some unnecessary imbalance. This amounts to being imprisoned by our choices. We then constantly feel like we are not living up to our potential, and don't have a clue why our efforts continually fall short.

Food Products

Early macrobiotic leaders helped bring healthy foods to North America and consistently worked to raise dietary consciousness. Prior to macrobiotics' introduction to North America, it would have been difficult to find foods like brown rice, miso, sea vegetables, and obscure vegetables like daikon or burdock. Before Bob Kennedy and Chico San you would not have been able to find a rice cake anywhere. Now they are in all major grocery stores, as is whole brown rice and quality soy sauce.

Macrobiotic proponents have worked over the last few decades to introduce healthy dietary practices and along the way endured considerable criticism and skepticism. Attempts to work with mainstream researchers and government departments have been peppered with some successes, but are more often rejected. An outstanding moment of change was the publication by the U.S. Senate Select Committee on Nutrition and Human Needs of *Dietary Goals for the United States* in 1977, informally known as the McGovern Report. This landmark report actually adhered closely to the primary dietary suggestions of macrobiotics at the time and that was the inclusion of complex (keyword) carbohydrates of 40-50 percent of dietary intake. The report generally recommended more vegetables, fruits, and whole grains, and less meat (although promoting more fish and poultry); fewer high-fat foods; less butter, eggs, and high-cholesterol foods; and less sugar and salt.

Complex carbohydrates are the key element here. Complex carbohydrates are the principal foods promoted by macrobiotic teachings and can have a far-reaching impact on planetary health, both on nutrition and on the environment, while helping to produce a sustainable food production/consumption system.

Dietary pronouncements change with the times and "facts" and "wisdom" are fluid as well. Of late, there is an opinion that saturated fat and high cholesterol foods are not culprits in the promotion of degenerative illnesses like cancer, heart disease, and diabetes after all, but it is really simple carbohydrates. This touches on one of the glaring omissions in the mainstream understanding of nutrition. Among the intelligentsia and average persons, the distinction between "complex" carbohydrates and "simple" carbohydrates is fuzzy at best. Often, all carbohydrates are lumped together in popular consciousness so that refined sugar (simple) and brown rice (complex) are both viewed as equal. As such, a negative connotation of complex carbohydrates has persisted.

The retraction of saturated fat and high cholesterol foods as health endangering foods is a mistake. These foods are still too energetically dense to be consumed in much quantity without creating physiological imbalances that will eventually lead to pathological conditions. Meanwhile, lumping all carbohydrates together obscures the overwhelming value of complex carbohydrates like whole grains and fails to differentiate the role of refined and simple carbohydrates in promoting degenerative illnesses.

Macrobiotics, rightly, draws upon the evolution of humans and the accompanying dietary patterns to posit that complex carbohydrates have sustained human life for a very long time. Whole natural plant-based foods with small amounts of animal foods have sustained humans for thousands of years.

The introduction of refined, processed, partial foods (sometimes referred to as "food-like substances") is, in evolutionary terms, a very recent addition to the human diet. We have not had time to adapt or to integrate these relatively novel foods into our evolutionary development, if indeed we ever can. They are so debased, contain so little vital energy, and contain so much toxicity that humans are likely to go extinct before adapting.

Macrobiotics introduced the notion of a principal, staple food—whole grains (complex carbohydrates)—and has remained steadfast in that position. I continue to consider that recommendation to be one of the most beneficial practices promoted by macrobiotics.

Macrobiotic Dietary Principles not the Macrobiotic Diet

Macrobiotics is distinguished from the thousands of "diets" out there in that it is not really a diet, but rather dietary principles. Even within macrobiotic circles the distinction between diet and dietary principles is not well known. I so often hear someone say, "That's not macro," meaning that whatever food is being considered is not part of a macrobiotic diet. My belief is that no one can pronounce a food "not macro" because one never knows the specific personal circumstances of an individual or what that person might require in a given moment as an appropriate dietary choice.

On this point I would once again invoke Ohsawa's notion of freedom. My interpretation of his idea of freedom is that each person eats according to macrobiotic principles to improve one's health and well being in pursuit of one's dream. That is not to say that one would eat something like cupcakes with abandon. Assuming the goal is to maintain physical health and well-being, consciousness of limitation and knowledge of macrobiotic dietary principles guide us as to how many, how often, and what kind of cupcakes, if any, we can eat and still maintain physical health and well-being. According to macrobiotic dietary principles, any one of these choices could be used in a macrobiotic way in unique circumstances.

The notions of personal uniqueness, personal goals, and adaptable macrobiotic dietary principles are essential components in making dietary decisions. Non-toxic, strengthening, high-quality principal and specialty foods consumed using macrobiotic principles give us the tools needed to succeed with our goals. To be quite honest, any "diet" that neither has the tools of refinement to match food and cooking choices to personal uniqueness nor the adaptability to be modified as a person's condition or circumstances change will, at best, have limited success.

Chapter 8

Macrobiotic Dietary Misconceptions

It may seem like a small detail, but the difference between *the* macrobiotic diet and *a* macrobiotic diet is significant. *The* macrobiotic diet implies that there is one standard, with a prescriptive set of dietary rules. *A* macrobiotic diet allows that there are many possible macrobiotic "diets" using macrobiotic *principles* for guidance in determining an individual's dietary practice. *The* diet communicates uniformity and inflexibility and *a* diet accommodates interpretation of macrobiotic dietary principles for individual needs.

There is nothing wrong with a macrobiotic approach to diet. It is the details of the standard macrobiotic formulation of yin/yang and the resulting misapplication of macrobiotic principles that has created problems for those attempting to pursue a macrobiotic diet and lifestyle. For reasons detailed in the chapter entitled, "Macrobiotics Is Not a Medical Modality," it is the over use and extended use of macrobiotic principles as a cooling, draining, cleansing, dispersing dietary practice that in time leads to deficiency.

Energetically speaking, it is the lack of fire energy in someone's macrobiotic practice that can create deficiency. Without sufficient fire energy, food and many nutrients cannot be assimilated. Lack of fire energy is like trying to cook without heat. In a simplified metaphoric TCM version, the transformation of food into blood is pictured as the stomach and small intestine sending food energy to the spleen where the spleen is rcpresented by a big kettle. Under the kettle is a log fire. The log fire is kidney yang/fire energy. The fire heats the kettle and the steam (food Qi) rises from the stomach/spleen to combine with air Qi from the lungs to form blood that is then sent to the heart for distribution (circulation).

Without sufficient fire energy from the kidney yang, the Qi from food is unavailable for the formation of blood and over time, deficiency of Blood, and eventually Qi, Yin, and Essence deficiency may develop. As a result, mal-absorption syndromes like weak/sensitive digestion and allergies can develop (when spleen energy is weak). I'll never forget that when I first went to TCM school (then 15 years into a dedicated macrobiotic practice) I had to sit by an open door during lecture classes because the fumes from the whiteboard markers made me nauseous and faint. It is interesting to recall that after I began to make dietary modifications and included more fire energy foods, that sensitivity went away.

In my view, something similar has happened for many macrobiotic adherents over the years. Many long time macrobiotic practitioners have developed weak, cold, and frail conditions.

Too Much…Too Little

The initial macrobiotic formulations stretching back to the 1960s that largely have remained unchanged ever since contain four significant imbalances.

#1: Too much salt

I used to joke that the Japanese have kidneys the size of footballs. An island country surrounded by salt water, salty air, sea vegetables… it stands to reason that the Japanese would develop a high tolerance for salt over the millennia. For nearly everyone else (especially of European descent), the Japanese-inspired macrobiotic dietary recommendations probably contain too much salt. As I learned in a physiology class, the body (and kidneys in particular) labors far more to deal with excess salt than it does with excess water.

Regarding the view that excess fluid/water weakens the body, I think macrobiotic theory is in error and is at odds with physiology. The macrobiotic pronouncement on fluid or water consumption is that drinking too much water dilutes the blood and makes someone's condition too yin and possibly weakens the kidneys. However, my understanding of physiology is that excess fluid increases blood volume whenever other factors are out of balance and not just when consuming lots of water. If someone drinks a lot of water with other factors in balance, mostly the water just passes through the "plumbing" and doesn't accomplish effective hydration.

Salt is a micronutrient, not a major food group. George Ohsawa would boast of eating nearly a fist full of salt to cure whatever ailment he would protract—an example of his extreme views and experimentations. This could be Ohsawa's Samurai teaching style at work. He impressed by excessive and bombastic statements attempting to awaken people from their unthinking stupor. Earnest aspiring macrobiotic neophytes tried to follow his example. Maybe not a fist full of salt, but the take away was that more salt is good. A young woman, who worked at Ponce Bakery in Chico, California back in the early 1990s where they made the most delectable cake called Japonais, referred to Herman Aihara as the "salty dog." I once asked Herman what to do for insomnia, "Add a little more salt," he said. At the time, gomashio was made with one teaspoon of salt per cup of sesame seeds. Now, I use a pinch to 1/8 teaspoon of salt for one cup of sesame seeds and it still tastes plenty salty to me.

We habituate to the taste of salt. That means the more salt we eat, the more salt we require to satisfy the taste for salt. No wonder the residents at the Vega Study Center would be sneaking off to Chico for ice cream, and secretly quaffing beers after hours trying to balance the intense salt concentration in the food. My first year at the French Meadows Summer Camp in 1989 with the high elevation, Cornellia inspired meals, and the infamous Ojia (leftovers cooked with additional salt), I felt tight and irritable the whole time from eating so much salt.

Once you back off the over-salted food that is also in the Standard American Diet, your corrupted and perverted palate calms down to what is normal for you, you will discover that you can be satisfied with very little salt. The rule of thumb then is, if it tastes salty, it is probably too salty; if it tastes bland, it is probably not salty enough. Every person is different.

#2 Too much pressure cooked short grain brown rice

Over-emphasizing yang qualities in preparing brown rice—short grain, pressure cooked, heavily salted—results in a grain preparation that is difficult to digest. The fiber content requires marathon chewing. If one follows the recommended 50 percent-plus grain portion size, brown rice will dominate the meal. This kind of meal can be congesting to the digestive tract. Consuming so much pressure cooked short grain brown rice may result in unbalanced nutrition.

My perception is that macrobiotic teaching stresses brown rice as a panacea of health. Some people who come in contact with macrobiotics may attempt the #7 diet, which is 100 percent grain and specific condiments for three to ten days as a cleanse. "Whatever ails you, the #7 diet is the cure" is the implication, if not explicit recommendation.

Another rather odd contradiction is that macrobiotic theory suggests to eat locally grown and in-season foods along with ancestral foods that one's grandparents and great-grandparents ate. For people of European descent, especially of Northern European descent, rice is an unfamiliar food, both in not being locally grown and in not being much consumed by their ancestors. This is an example of cultural bias favoring the Asian (Japanese) history of rice as a staple grain and food. Macrobiotic principles should be applied to local and ancestral circumstances to make an appropriate modification by each person. Brown rice is still somewhat of an unfamiliar food to most Western people.

The Standard Macrobiotic Diet recommendations emphasize a high percentage of any grain (short grain brown rice in particular) to excess. Too much salt and grain stresses the internal organs and excess fiber wears out the digestive organs so that, although mounds of grain/rice are consumed, very little energy is assimilated, resulting in weight loss, low energy, constant hunger, and lack of satisfaction from eating.

#3 Too little fluid

People in North American society have a very competitive nature. We are obsessed with records and champions and with being number one. In America, if a certain amount is good, more is better, and too much is just right. We are a young culture and our egos are very strong. As a culture we like to compete at everything. Early macrobiotic recommendations included drinking as little fluid as possible so as to strengthen the kidneys. Herman Aihara was known as "the kidney man" since he frequently talked about kidney health. He claimed that he only ate miso soup and brown rice and drank very little water, maybe a little bancha tea. Some early macrobiotic followers, some of whom lived in study houses in Boston, would compete with each other to see how few times a day they needed to urinate. Drinking very little and urinating two times for women and three times for men per day was thought to be a sign of health and drew praise from macrobiotic teachers and followers. The thinking was that there is plenty of liquid in miso soup, rice, and vegetables to provide sufficient hydration. To me, this is one of the patterns that contributed to the development of deficiency. Human beings are 75 percent fluid. Considerable fluid resources are expended in perspiration and respiration. Cornellia was fond of saying that we lose one cup of fluid every night through breathing and perspiration. By severely limiting fluid intake, one's interior condition becomes desiccated and dehydrated over time. A common condition among long-time macrobiotic practitioners is the TCM version of Yin and Blood deficiency, both of which are an extreme form of dehydration and internal dryness. This internal dryness is eventually expressed as symptoms such as dry skin, dry hair, dry eyes, insufficient fluids, be it saliva or vaginal secretions, and eventually registers as fatigue and low energy. Appropriate hydration is covered in Chapter 11 on Physical Healing. Generally speaking, many people practicing a macrobiotic diet consume too little fluid and become dehydrated.

#4 Too little fat and protein

Macrobiotic books contend that 450 grams of rice has enough

protein and that adding beans and a little bit of oil in cooking along with some seeds provide enough fat to support health. However, my observation is that some people can't access enough nutrition with limited protein and fat such that the body slowly suffers from malnutrition.

While there might be some individuals who by force of constitution, will, or divine intervention can maintain a healthy and strong body on a high-grain-low-fat/protein diet, many people cannot. I suggest people cut back on grain by eating a smaller portion of grains at meals along with generous portions of vegetables and some form of protein and fat every day. There are no set amounts for protein and fat. The appropriate amount of fat and protein for an individual must be decided at the *individual* level. I can't emphasize enough that this can only be arrived at by each individual developing good judgment.

It may be necessary to rely on teachers, counselors, and books early on in macrobiotic practice. However, the role of such resources is training, not dependence. Ideally, as one studies, learns, and experiments in his or her own macrobiotic practice, good judgment and intuition will develop and appropriate choices can be made independent of counselors and teachers.

Vegan/Vegetarian Dietary Practices

Plant-based diets make sense from so many perspectives. A plant-based diet is far more efficient at delivering calories than a diet high in animal products. We are all familiar with the huge amount of resources required to produce animal protein. The cruelty and drug-aided raising of animals has been well documented. We should all be striving to eat a more plant-based diet for the sake of our health and for the survival of our civilization and our planet.

Essential Developments

To realize the vision of a planetary plant-based diet, a couple of essential developments must take place. First, each of us needs to improve the strength of our digestion. This is something we can do right now. Weak digestion is one of the conditions that prevents people from having success with a plant-based diet. People get inspired by the concept of a plant-based diet, move directly into a strictly vegan or vegetarian diet, and after their excesses are cleared, they begin to develop symptoms of deficiency. The reasons are at least twofold: one, their digestion is not strong enough (to begin with) to sufficiently digest and assimilate (i.e., build blood) a plant-based diet; and two, when digestion is not strong, there is not enough fire energy in a plant-based diet to promote the transformation of all that high-quality plant-based food into accessible qi and blood. Internal organs then become weaker over time.

Second, the quality of our environment and the quality of our food needs to improve. For many years now the environment, the soil, and hence the food supply have become progressively devitalized. We have succeeded in rendering food appealing to the eyes and seemingly to taste, but at the same time have reduced the vitality and the energy of that food. Conscientious stewardship of our land and productive resources is absolutely essential. Strides are being made but much more needs to be done. Meanwhile, we must survive and thrive to make these changes happen. For some people to realize these goals, an appropriate consumption of animal-based food is helpful. Animal-derived foods not only provide restorative nutrition, but also help to strengthen the internal organs to do their functions more efficiently. Animal-derived foods, especially those from hot-blooded animals, provide the fire energy that helps transform all food nutrients into blood and thus the energy and resources to strengthen all internal organs, tissues, and systems, including the brain.

Animal Food—A Contradiction?

There is a sharp distinction between the common American consumption of animal foods and what I am suggesting. Surely, a large slab of flesh like a steak with only a sprig of parsley or a small dinner salad is truly toxic, even if it is grass fed, organic, free range and was talked to lovingly right up to its slaughter. Such a high concentration of protein and fat is acid forming and toxic. There is a principle in macrobiotic theory that "quantity changes quality." The amount and proportion of animal food in the above example is toxic. Conversely, a bed of brown rice with many vegetables on top and a small amount of animal protein is going to be far less toxic, if at all. The alkaline-forming vegetables offset the acidity of the smaller amount of animal protein. An appropriate meat portion complemented with vegetables, grains, soup, and sea vegetables is an appropriate and effective application of macrobiotic dietary principles (7 yin to 1 yang ratio), especially for a deficient condition.

Animal Essence

It is even better and more effective to incorporate hot-blooded animal essence in one's diet. The real strength of animal food is not necessarily in its flesh and macronutrients of fat and protein. Animal essence, particularly hot-blooded animal quality, has the capability of tonifying the internal organs to do their tasks with greater efficiency. People who have eaten a vegan/vegetarian diet of mostly cooling foods, and even those who use warming cooking styles, can still develop weak digestion from the digestive fire being slowly diminished over the years. These people have usually developed a cold nature (cold hands and feet most of the time) and accumulated dampness in their bodies (puffy water retention-like weight) due to diminished capacity to transform fluid and food into blood and energy. A few weeks of bone-stock soup and most people experience improvement in their condition. An explanation and more details of how to prepare bone broths is included in Chapter 11 on Physical Healing.

Macrobiotics is Not a Vegan/Vegetarian Dietary Practice

While macrobiotic principles can be applied to create a vegan and/or a vegetarian diet for someone's condition that can handle it, macrobiotic dietary theory is not, and never has been, exclusively vegan and/or vegetarian. What is important, actually crucial, is the application of macrobiotic dietary principles to make appropriate dietary choices for the condition and goals of the person in question.

And sometimes, for some people, that might mean the inclusion of animal-sourced food. There are ten diets in Ohsawa's *Zen Macrobiotics* chapter on Ten Healthful Ways of Eating and Drinking (p. 50) and five of them include small amounts of animal food.

Chapter 9

Making a Macrobiotic Diet Work

Many people get overwhelmed with the details of a macrobiotic dietary practice. It is true that for someone new to macrobiotics some of the foods sound strange. I have observed many a knitted brow when I say, "miso." And, that's way before foods like daikon, ume, or natto enters the conversation. Often, people get the impression that all the foreign and strange sounding foods, cooking techniques, and theory have to be mastered and practiced in their entirety and to perfection to pursue a macrobiotic dietary practice. For most folks, this sets them up for frustration and feelings of failure. What follows is an attempt at a simplified yet effective approach to macrobiotic dietary practice.

Principles

Warming and Cooling

One of the most basic principles of macrobiotics is the notion of complementary opposites, most recognizable as *yin and yang*. In teaching macrobiotic dietary practice I like to apply the complementary opposite theory in the form of *warming and cooling*. Here I want to limit the discussion of warming/cooling to practical applications for making a macrobiotic diet effective, i.e., self-assessment, food energy, and cooking styles. Basically, use warming energies to address cold conditions; cooling energies for hot conditions.

Warming		Cooling
Oats, spelt, quinoa, sweet brown rice, mochi	**Grains**	millet, barley, wheat, amaranth
kale, cabbage, onion, leek, parsnip, winter squash, scallion, ginger, parsley	**Vegetables**	cauliflower, broccoli, summer squash, lettuce, bok choy, sweet corn, celery, zucchini, daikon radish, sweet potato
cherry, citrus peel, date	**Fruits**	apple, pear, persimmon, watermelon, all citrus
trout, salmon, chicken, beef, lamb, ghee	**Animal**	milk, ice cream, yogurt, kefir

Self Assessment

Heat condition: Person feels hot, dislikes heat, attracted to cold, has red face, red eyes, bright red tongue, yellow coating on tongue, and bad breath. Such a person may have high blood pressure, fast heart rate, inflammation, sores, and eruptions such as acne. Tends to be constipated and have dark yellow urine both with strong odor, mucus and phlegm are thick and yellow or green. Personality tends to be aggressive, loud, and insensitive.

Cold condition: Person feels cold, dislikes cold, attracted to heat and is often overdressed and wants warm food and drinks, pale complexion, slow heart rate. Tends toward loose stools and diarrhea, clear urine, and thin watery mucus. Personality tends to be shy, quiet, and (over) sensitive.

Food Energy

In General: Animal food is warmer than plant food. Oils are generally warming; sesame, coconut, and ghee are good for cooking, raw olive oil for salad dressings. Plants that take longer to grow are more warming. Foods that are blue, green, or purple are more cooling; red, orange, and yellow are more warming. Some foods such as carrot, brown rice, corn, and buckwheat are considered "neutral" but, as with all foods, are influenced by cooking style.

Cooking Styles from more warming to more cooling:

Pressure cooking, long boiling, baking, pan frying, deep frying, broiling, quick sautéing, light boiling, steaming, and raw.

For a more information on warming/cooling energies/foods consult *Healing with Whole Foods*, by Paul Pitchford.

Locally Grown/In Season

Appropriate energy for one's condition/needs/purpose is a fundamental principle of macrobiotics. When thinking of foods to buy and prepare, think "locally grown, in season, and/or naturally preserved." Locally grown as a rule of thumb is what is available in a 500 mile north to south band. Such a swath of latitude generally shares similar climate features and will produce a similar range of food products. What is growing in your area right now? What are the seasonal vegetables? What can be naturally preserved? The theory of note here is that whatever grows in your region has successfully adapted to the environmental conditions there. If you consume these foods, they impart the ability to adapt successfully to the conditions where you live.

Vitality of Food

If you are standing in front of a case filled with bunches of kale and you are selecting some for your dinner that night, you wouldn't pick a limp, slightly brown bunch if there is a hearty, crisp, rich-green looking and feeling bunch there too. Sort of common sense right? Part visual, part tactile, part smell, part intuition is the recognition of vitality in foods when shopping. Think to yourself. "What item in the midst of others looks the most alive!"

Energy of the Cook

The mental, emotional, and spiritual temperament of the cook is a subtle but significant influence on the nourishing quality of foods. If the cook is centered, grounded, calm, kind, and loving, the food served will carry those energies. Conversely, if the cook is scattered, flighty, upset, or mean-spirited the food served will carry those energies. Ideally, food is prepared at the household level by the central earth-energy figure in the household, someone who knows and loves each member of the household and can make changes in the foods prepared to support the needs of each member.

Limit Refined, Fragmented, Manufactured Foods/Energies

I have found that, initially, it is what people eliminate from their diets that has the most positive effect on health. One of the wonders of healing power is that it always trends to equilibrium and health, if given a chance. Removing the impediments allows healing power to have an immediate impact.

In modern times, processed food is everywhere and seemingly

inexpensive and convenient. Processed food is so heavily advertised and marketed it would seem almost un-American not to consume such "food-like" substances. Don't be deceived. These foods are so far from nutritious and nourishing that they can't really be considered food. They might fill the stomach, but they do not nourish. It is well known that fast-food producers craft their foods to create more desire for their products, not actually to nourish. The mass-produced meat and dairy industries are deep into unhealthy practices; antibiotics, hormones, squalid growing conditions…enough said.

We evolved and have adapted to whole, natural foods over millennia. When we ingest a fragmented, refined food, it is as if our body/mind/spirit goes into mourning or panic. We seek (crave) the missing part and end up chasing our cravings until we have gained much weight and made ourselves sick. Furthermore, energetically speaking, fragmented foods create fragmented consciousness and promote fragmented unclear thinking, which leads to more unwholesome decisions. One's life can spiral into poor health and suffering.

Refined carbohydrates such as white (wheat) flour, white sugar, high-fructose corn syrup, and refined poor quality oils like partially hydrogenated oils and their derivatives are everywhere in manufactured foods. Then there are the "paragraphs" of ingredients in refined foods that are unpronounceable and are most often of manufactured chemical origin. These "foods" are to be avoided at all costs. They are literally poisonous. If a "food" comes in a package, read the ingredients very carefully. Shop around the walls of a grocery store where the fresh produce usually is displayed. Add whole grains, beans, etc. from the bulk bins and you will have acquired nourishing food. Organic unrefined sesame oil, coconut oil, ghee (for cooking), or olive oil (raw) can be used to support one's condition.. Small amounts of barley malt or rice syrup can be used as sweeteners.

Chaotic Life

Try to avoid/minimize over/under eating and unconscious

snacking, especially eating to deal with emotions, and eating late at night. As much as possible don't over/under work, don't over/under rest, and in general avoid a chaotic schedule. Too much or too little of anything will create an imbalance and devitalize life functions.

Simplify

Avoid complex refined foods and choose whole foods: grains, beans, vegetables, sea vegetables, fermented foods like miso and pickles, and good-quality fat and protein. If most or all of your meals consist of whole foods chosen from these categories, you are already well on your way to health and vitality.

Cook at home for your family and loved ones. Maintain a peaceful atmosphere around cooking and eating and chew well.

Eating meals, going to bed/rising, working, performing chores, and exercising at roughly the same times each day enables the body to operate efficiently. If activities are rhythmic, the body "knows" when it can rest and repair. If activities are chaotic, the body is stressed by the anxiety of deprivation and anticipation; it is always on alert ("fight or flight"). That drains energy unnecessarily.

Sufficient rest is crucial. If the body can't rest and repair itself, it goes into the next day with a deficit of energy and if that continues over a long time, eventually some function will break down.

Circulation of energy and blood supports and accomplishes all life functions. Moderate exercise promotes circulation of energy and blood. Exercise can be simple, doesn't require a gym or personal trainer. Brisk walking and gentle twisting and stretching exercises are sufficient.

Specific and Uncompromising

Cornellia Aihara used to say a macrobiotic diet is simple, but it is specific and uncompromising. I have found this to be true. Diet in general, and a macrobiotic diet in particular, is unique to each individual. Our constitutions and all the qualities that we have are unique; so, ultimately, each person's dietary practice will be slightly different from everyone else's. Don't get drawn into comparisons and competitions about who is "more macrobiotic." This is an ego concern and will likely lead you to an untruth about your own uniqueness.

Always be learning, studying, and increasing your knowledge. Your dietary practice will change with the seasons, age, and activity level. Don't be afraid to experiment. Discover what works for you. You decide. "See for yourself," as George Ohsawa said.

The uncompromising part is to stick to your resolve. Be dedicated to your goal of attaining good health and vitality. If you deviate and experience poor health, use it as a learning experience and return to your dietary practice with renewed vigor. Use the adventure of a macrobiotic diet to help you to evolve physically and spiritually.

Develop Good Judgment

In my view, developing good judgment is the heart of macrobiotics. Herman Aihara taught about understanding one's limitations. If we know our limitations and stay within them, then we have freedom to do what we like. If we consistently exceed our limitations we become enslaved to the consequences of our choices and our lives are consumed by trying to recover from the consequences.

It is of paramount importance to develop good judgment. I think we all know what good judgment feels like. It is "doing the right thing" that has a positive outcome. My suggestions are to study macrobiotics, to consult with a counselor for help if needed, and to apply macrobiotic principles to diet and lifestyle to support physical and spiritual evolution. Studying, seeking advice, and learning how to make good decisions all contribute to the nourishment of body, mind, and spirit. Making a good decision isn't that complicated. Frame your choices as an either/or proposition. Distill even the most complex decision down to two choices. At that level, one choice will feel more nourishing than the other. The more nourishing choices you make the better your health and vitality.

Ultimately, making a macrobiotic diet work for you is a process of informed trial and error. Start with what you know, try it out, and see what works. If something works for you, keep doing it until it doesn't work, and then move on to another choice. If something doesn't work for you, don't do it. You can try it again later, but strive to be clear about how something affects you. Be true to yourself and over time you will build an effective dietary practice and a happy and healthy life.

Chapter 10

Everything Starts with Digestion

As discussed in Chapter 8, two of the essential changes that each of us can do right now are; one, move toward a more plant-based diet; and two, enhance assimilation and vitality by improving digestion. Improving digestion is an essential primary step in realizing positive results with a macrobiotic diet.

Everyone would like to enjoy vibrant health and vitality—to have boundless energy, a clear mind, and a strong and resilient body. The essential challenge that we all face in achieving health and vitality is transforming the external environment into our internal environment. This involves the digestion, transformation, and assimilation of foods and fluids into blood, cells, tissues, and organs. The strength and efficiency of digestion determines the degree of vitality that we experience. With effective digestion, foods and fluids can be transformed into strong blood. Strong blood nourishes and vitalizes the cells, flesh, bones, and internal organs and in turn strengthens and vitalizes the mind and spirit.

Digestion encompasses several general areas: internal organs must be functioning efficiently, foods and beverages must be selected and prepared for maximum bioavailability, and the techniques and conditions of eating and drinking must be selected and practiced according to the needs of the individual.

The specific function of digestion is to transform substances from the environment outside of our bodies to usable material and energy inside our bodies. The physical process of digestion can be organized into three phases: preparation, assimilation, and elimination. These three phases are linked in sequence, i.e., the sequence has to keep moving liking cars of a train coupled together. If there is a break down, a slow down, or inefficiency anywhere along the sequence, the vitality of the body, mind, and spirit is diminished.

Preparation

Our bodies have rhythms. When those rhythms are maintained, all systems have the best opportunity to function most efficiently. Eating meals at roughly the same time each day sets up a rhythm that the body responds to. If our digestive organs and related systems can count on meals showing up at regular times, our digestive secretions activate and deactivate in anticipation of that regularity. The digestive system can relax between meals and conserve energy to effectively transform the next meal. If mealtimes are erratic, the digestive system stays in a state of confusion and anxiety. This kind of erratic pattern keeps the digestive system on high alert, a kind of "fight or flight," and keeps the digestive system active when it could be resting. Over time, the digestive system can become exhausted and digestion problems will ensue. It may not be possible in a busy and complicated world to be so regular all the time, but it is the prevalent rhythm over time that contributes to the quality of digestion.

Quality of food certainly effects digestion. Fresh, organic, whole foods are more likely to provide vital high-quality nutrition than their processed, manufactured, or refined counterparts. Minimizing or avoiding extreme and/or congesting foods laden with heavy fat, refined sugar, white flour, and excessive and poor quality salt and oil will promote better digestion.

For people living in a temperate climate, digestion is aided by a diet of primarily cooked food. Cooking transforms foods for easier digestion. This is especially important for people with weak digestion. While a variety of cooking styles, including raw foods, is beneficial, the fire energy that is added in cooking food assists the digestive process. This fire energy not only renders food easier to digest but also strengthens the digestive organs.

Simple meals place the least stress on the digestive organs, particularly the stomach. Too many types of foods, too many tastes, or too many spices/sauces can create enzyme confusion and may result in indigestion or reaching for Tums and Maalox. Furthermore, no matter what we eat, the stomach's job is to turn everything to a soup/stew texture. The closer the texture of food is to soup or stew, the less stress placed on the stomach.

Stomach, spleen, and pancreas are considered part of the Earth element in Traditional Chinese Medicine. Emphasizing Earth energy stomach/spleen friendly foods can aid digestion. Earth energy corresponds to sweet taste, and complex carbohydrate sweet is best—whole grains (millet, brown rice), squash, sweet potatoes, carrots, and garbanzo beans.

Finally, the state of mind and energy of the cook will make a difference in the digestibility and vitality of food. Optimally, food is prepared at home with the cook occupying a central (Earth energy) role in the family. Food mindfully prepared by a loving cook in a peaceful environment will be nourishing and strengthening. Contrast this to food that is prepared in a fast food restaurant. The difference in the energy of the food as well as taste is significant.

Assimilation

One of the functions of digestion that we have the most control over is chewing. Chewing well, at least 50 times per mouthful, thoroughly mixes food with saliva and begins the digestive process inside our bodies. Chewing is one's last chance to render that external environment—the "not you" into the "you" that is one's internal environment. By chewing well, we can make food our own so that the tasks of assimilation further down the digestive tract are less stressful and more efficient.

In line with the ideas of rhythm, it is best not to overeat or to eat late at night. Overeating, even of high-quality vital food, overwhelms the entire digestive system and can cause bloating, gas, reflux, and other discomforts. It is tempting to use food as an emotional comfort and from time to time we all do it; but, if it is a regular habit overeating could be a sign that something else is out of balance. I once heard someone say we should get love from each other, not from food.

Nighttime is when the liver is most active, particularly in its function of purifying blood. Energetically, blood returns to the liver at night to "rest," which promotes good quality sleep. Eating late at night redirects the body's energy, particularly blood, to the stomach. If blood is redirected away from the liver to the stomach at this time, the result is likely to be insomnia and a backlog of blood purification. Sluggishness and fatigue may follow the next day.

Digestive enzymes present in or accompanying food promotes assimilation. Many cultures around the world have some form of traditional fermented food that provides helpful digestive enzymes. Pickles, miso, soy sauce, sauerkraut, tempeh, kimchi, natto, and kombucha are a few examples.

Food combining can help maximize digestion/assimilation. A primarily plant-based diet following macrobiotic dietary principles pretty much ensures positive food combining. There is so much information on food combining that I refer readers to investigate other sources such as *Healing with Whole Foods* by Paul Pitchford.

Another strategy for addressing food combining is to prepare one-pot meals. The long cooking of soups and stews does the food combining in the cooking process for effective digestion and assimilation.

Coffee is best avoided for several reasons, but with regard to digestion, the acids in coffee can damage the villi in the small intestine and inhibit assimilation. Conversely, a variation of ume-sho-kuzu known as Morning Tea (from Herman and Cornellia Aihara) is powerfully alkalizing to all body fluids and supports good digestion, assimilation, and elimination.

Morning Tea

1 rounded tsp kuzu (more if a thicker consistency is desired)
2 Tbsp cool water

½ tsp soy sauce (low sodium is preferred)
1 soybean sized drop of ume concentrate (not plums or paste)
¼ tsp ginger juice (squeezed from fresh grated ginger pulp)
1 cup boiling bancha tea

Directions:

In a cup, dissolve kuzu in 2 tablespoons cool water. Add soy sauce and stir to make brownish slurry. Add one cup boiling bancha tea while stirring the slurry. It should go from opaque to clear as the kuzu warms from the boiling tea. Add the ginger juice and stir in the ume concentrate. Let cool a bit and drink.

Another time-tested home remedy that aids digestion is the venerable ginger compress. Ginger's energy penetrates and radiates. The application of a warm ginger compress over the stomach and intestines stimulates the flow of blood and energy in those digestive organs and assists and strengthens their functions. Refer to *Natural Healing from Head to Toe* by Cornellia and Herman Aihara with Carl Ferré or *Macrobiotics Today* (May/June 1994) for instructions on how to prepare and apply a ginger compress.

Elimination

The final phase of digestion is elimination, often overlooked because we tend to focus on the stomach and small intestines activities of nutrient acquisition. Returning to the train analogy, if the front of the train is sluggish the whole train slows down. So it is with elimination. Food material retained in the large intestines can compact and create toxic materials. Also, if the transit of material in the large intestive slows down, the function of the entire digestive tract slows down, just like an engine with the brakes on slows down a train.

If we have a healthy dietary practice regarding the preparation and assimilation phases of digestion, likely good elimination will follow. However, if there are problems with elimination, there are a few simple practices that can help.

Emphasizing elimination-friendly textures in food choices and cooking styles aids elimination. Soft moist whole grains in the form of porridge or congee for breakfast provides ample fluid and fiber to promote smooth movement of material through the digestive tract. Soups and stews prepared with vegetables, beans, sea vegetables, and whole grains also promote smooth elimination. Cooked fruit like apples, pears, or prunes can help to lubricate the intestines and promote ease of elimination. Inclusion of the mucilaginous sea vegetables, especially wakame or alaria, will lubricate, cool, and moisten the linings of the digestive tract and are especially beneficial for those who have any kind of inflammation in stomach or intestines. Earth energy foods like baked squash and sweet potatoes promote smooth transit; for example, a preparation of 2-parts millet, 2-parts butternut squash, and 1-part garbanzo beans.

Walking after eating can assist the movement of material through the digestive system. Walking massages the intestines and it is said that walking a thousand paces uphill after dinner promotes good digestion and assimilation. Indeed, walking uphill stimulates the stomach acupuncture meridian, which runs across the top of the foot and up the leg.

Abdominal breathing also massages the digestive organs and supports the peristaltic wave that moves food material along the digestive tract. The peristaltic wave that is initiated with swallowing sets up an energy flow that follows through to elimination. As such, when the "urge to go" comes it is advantageous to answer the call as soon as possible. If the wave is suppressed, it may disrupt the rhythm of the wave allowing digestive material to stagnate.

Abdominal massage and ginger compresses will strengthen and stimulate the function of the digestive organs, particularly the intestines, and aid in elimination. Lastly, sitting quietly in a reflective state of mind with the spine upright and utilizing the breath and a downward release of tension in the abdomen aids elimination.

A Final Word

Digestion, assimilation, and elimination are among the first functions to address when someone is attempting to heal and strengthen his or her health. These functions transform the outside environment into the blood that nourishes all cells and ultimately all physiological functions. If digestion is healthy, we have the best chance to experience health and vitality in body, mind, and spirit.

PART 3

HEALING BODY AND SOUL

Chapter 11

Physical Healing

Healing requires a strong immune system. Immune system strength is measured by the ability to maintain equilibrium in the body's vital functions and to respond to extraordinary challenges to that equilibrium. There are many perspectives on what comprises the immune system. It can be viewed as a physical biochemical function of bacteria, antibodies, T-cells, and mineral balance or as the strength and condition of vital organs such as poor digestion/ elimination, leaky gut, or weak kidneys. The energetic (as opposed to the physical) view considers the acquisition, incorporation, and elimination of several types of energy including food, mental, emotional, and spiritual. This chapter focuses on physical healing practices regarding immune system strength and *physical* healing power. The following chapter focuses on mental, emotional, and spiritual practices regarding immune system strength and *energetic* healing power.

Circulation is the Thing

One of the most important aspects of health and healing is circulation—the bearing of blood, nutrients, micronutrients, and energy (life force) to the cells and the transporting of byproducts of cell activity away from the cells for elimination. In the midst of this process the cell miraculously transforms nutrients and energy into "life," that which animates and invigorates the cells, tissues, and organs and creates our living body, mental thoughts, and spiritual being. On a relatively superficial level, think of a waiter bringing food to a table at a restaurant, a person eating, and the staff coming around later to take away the dishes. Such is circulation.

Diet is Necessary, but...

Supportive dietary practice is a necessary condition for strengthening the immune system, i.e., without supportive dietary practice the immune system can't remain strong long term. At the same time, a healthy diet is not *sufficient* to ensure a strong immune system. Eliminating weakening foods and beverages make the strongest impact on immune system strength, at least at first. Other factors like mental rigidity, emotional stuck spots, and/or spiritual energy need to be addressed as well.

Sugar

To strengthen a weak immune system, reduce or eliminate all sugar and simple, refined carbohydrates. By sugar, I mean virtually all kinds of sweeteners: refined sugar, brown sugar, raw sugar, corn syrup, molasses, honey, maple syrup, agave syrup, and even organic evaporated cane juice. Refined foods of almost every description, but especially refined flour products, breads, pastries, and pasta must be eliminated, too. All alcoholic beverages also are best eliminated. For very deficient immune systems even rice syrup, barley malt syrup, fruit and fruit juices, and amasake are best avoided/eliminated.

Dairy

Dairy products are difficult for most people to fully metabolize and are congesting. Congesting foods significantly contribute to physical constraint, particularly in the respiratory system, and stress the immune system. People with frequent colds and kids with recurring ear infections often show marked improvement when they eliminate dairy products. Dairy products include milk, butter, cheese, cottage cheese, ice cream, kefir, and yogurt. When I suggest eliminating dairy products to someone, he or she will often say, "But you don't mean yogurt do you?" Yes, I do mean yogurt. Fermented cultures notwithstanding, yogurt can still result in congestion, constraint, and immune system stress in someone with a weak immune system. Clarified butter or ghee can be tolerated and digested well by some.

Foods that Go Crunch

We Americans enjoy a crispy crunchy texture. Food manufacturers calculate specific values of pounds of pressure per square inch that are used in making corn and potato chips so that when we bite down it has just the right resistance to deliver that satisfying "crunch". However, dry, hard, crispy, salty snacks take a heavy toll on the body's reserves of fluids. The stomach must transform what we eat it into a soup texture. Dry, hard, crispy foods tax the body's store of fluids, negatively impact circulation and in turn weaken the equilibrium of the immune system. Even rice cakes, corn thins, popcorn and other organic, natural crackers, chips, and crispy snacks are best avoided..

Bread and Flour Products

My mother was an accomplished baker, part of her German heritage. There were always baked goods in the house when I was growing up, including homemade (yeasted) bread. I have always been fond of good bread. Good bread nowadays means a naturally leavened, organic, whole grain variety where the grain has been ground just prior to being made into dough. However, even good bread can place a strain on a weak immune system. Flour products can be congesting and compacting in the colon, contributing to constipation; and, the moisture leeching quality of flour products can strain the stomach. While I believe good bread and whole grain flour products are healthy nourishing foods, I recommend avoiding all bread and baked flour products for someone with a weak immune system. Whole grain noodles like 100 percent buckwheat soba are less stressful to the immune system for most people.

Protein and Fatty Foods

Many animal products, even free-range, organic, grass-fed varieties are heavy and fatty and can cause congestion and constraint.

The low fiber content of animal flesh and the sludging of blood from fatty foods strain the immune system. If animal foods are thought to be necessary, lean poultry and fish may be tolerated. The animal product exception is nourishing and tonifying bone stock soups (see below). Fatty foods such as oils, nuts, seeds, and avocadoes, even the organic variety, if eaten in excess can have a congesting effect. I usually suggest flax oil or a little olive oil as a non-congesting source of fat.

Bone Stock Preparation

Request beef or chicken bones at the meat counter of a natural food store. I use 2 pounds of bones in a 4 liter pressure cooker. Rinse chicken/beef bones, place in a pressure cooker, and fill within 1 inch of the top with water. Add 4 three-inch pieces of wakame or alaria and two tablespoons rice vinegar. The wakame or alaria adds valuable minerals and the acidic rice vinegar pulls out the alkalizing minerals from the bones. Lock the lid on the pressure cooker and bring up to pressure. Cook for 4 hours over low heat. Remove from heat. (Or boil chicken/beef bones in water for 4 hours; more water will be needed than pressure-cooking.)

When the pressure comes all the way down, open the cooker. Remove and discard the bones. Pour the stock into a large container and cover. Place stock in the refrigerator overnight. The fat will rise to the top and harden.

The next day, skim off the hardened fat from the top. You can save the fat and add it back in soups or use in sautéing if desired. The fat can be a rich source of warmth and yin nourishment. Everything below the fat layer is the mineral- and nutrient-rich soup stock. Set aside 1½ cups of stock for immediate soup preparation. Pour the remaining soup stock into small containers (reused 1-pound plastic miso containers work well) and place in the freezer for ready-made future soup stock.

Soup Preparation

Use any soup/stew recipe you like. Wash, chop, and sauté

the vegetables. Stir in herbs/spices. Add chicken/beef soup stock, water (5-10 cups water per 1 cup stock; less for richer soup, more for thinner soup), add precooked rice and simmer for 10 minutes. If a creamy, thicker texture appeals to you, add a kuzu mixture (1 teaspoon kuzu dissolved in small amount of cool water per cup of soup) and stir. Add miso five minutes before serving. Pour into soup bowls, garnish with parsley.

Caffeine: The False Energy

Caffeine must be eliminated to strengthen the immune system for the long term. It is true that ingesting caffeine provides an energy lift, but it is with a price…always a front (something beneficial) has a back (potentially harmful). Caffeine is in coffee, black tea, sodas, and chocolate. Impact-wise, caffeine resembles a medicine more than a food. A medicine is narrowly focused, fast acting, and dramatic in effect. A medicine is appropriate to get though a crisis and to avoid the development of a more serious condition. Taken infrequently as a medicine, caffeine can be helpful. Used daily, it erodes immune system strength. Caffeine has the capability to convert stored reserve energy into active energy, hence the temporary boost of energy. However, caffeine leaves a deficit in its wake. Caffeine's affect is to "borrow from tomorrow to pay for today." I'm often asked if green tea and dark chocolate are exceptions. I leave these choices up to the individual, but my feeling is that any caffeine product depletes the immune system and healing power.

Macrobiotics to the Rescue

Macrobiotic dietary principles tailored to an individual's condition can be an effective dietary strategy to strengthen healing power and the immune system. Here is a sample list of foods:

Whole grains/Complex Carbohydrates

- Brown rice, millet
- Baked squash, sweet potatoes
- Root vegetables—carrots, turnips, daikon, burdock

Vegetables

- Cauliflower, broccoli, sweet corn, green beans, peas, celery
- Leafy greens—kale & collard greens

Good Quality Fat

- Sesame oil
- Olive oil
- Flax oil
- English walnuts, almonds, sunflower and pumpkin seeds

Good Quality Protein

- Lentils, chickpeas, adzuki, other beans
- Tempeh
- Fish—wild caught cod, trout, salmon
- Chicken

Sea Vegetables

- alaria, wakame, kombu, arame, nori

Fermented Foods

- Takuan (daikon pickle), other pickles
- Sauerkraut
- Natto
- Miso, soy sauce, tamari

Additional foods can be added by referring to any basic macrobiotic book. Some of the above foods will not be suitable for all conditions; other foods may need to be added. I stress that personalized application of macrobiotic dietary principles will yield better results than "the" standard macrobiotic diet. To effectively apply macrobiotic dietary principles requires study, practice, and experimentation. Guidance from an experienced counselor can be helpful at first.

Furthermore, foods should be of organic quality, meals should be eaten at regular times, and late-night eating (three hours before bed) and unconscious snacking must be minimized or eliminated.

Hydration

The human body is mostly fluid (up to 75% of body weight) and assimilation and circulation of fluids is essential to healing power and immune system strength. Whatever fluid is ingested must be assimilable all the way to the cells. Fluids that contain some kind of mineral content provide effective hydration. One of the most effective hydrating fluids is a good solid miso soup like the following recipe. I have found South River Miso Company one-year Chickpea Miso easy to assimilate.

Miso Soup

1 tsp toasted sesame oil
½ tsp grated ginger
1 scallion chopped
2 cups water
1 tsp miso to taste

Sauté ginger and scallion in oil until fragrant. Add 1½ cups water, bring to near boil. Dissolve miso in ½ cup water, add to soup, simmer a few minutes and serve.

The following green drink is also good for hydration:

Green Drink

1 Tbsp liquid chlorophyll
¼ cup aloe vera juice
¾ cup water

Combine all ingredients and drink warm or room temperature.

Other good hydrating beverages are spring water with a dash of sea salt and/or lemon and herbal teas, especially mint and chamomile. The morning tea recipe in Chapter 10 on digestion is another good choice for hydration, but reduce soy sauce (salty taste) if using more than once a day so as not to stress the kidneys.

Other Lifestyle Factors

As stated earlier, diet is necessary, but is not sufficient, to strengthen the immune system. Rest and rejuvenating sleep are also very important. In my experience, insufficient rest/sleep is common these days. Everyone is trying to cram more into a day than her or his immune system can manage. Nowadays, people are chronically tired, exhausted, and depleted, a condition that seriously undermines healing power and the strength of the immune system. When we are under-rested, reserves have to be tapped to keep going. Depletion of reserves equates to weakening healing power and the immune system.

To facilitate circulation of energy and blood and thus strengthen healing power and the immune system, moderate exercise is helpful. A combination of light aerobic exercise like brisk walking and stretching/twisting exercises like yoga or Tai Qi will support healing power and the immune system strength.

Moderation in sexual activity prevents weakening the immune system. Too frequent ejaculation in men and pregnancies too close together are definitions of sexual excess in Traditional Chinese Medicine (TCM). The frequency and depleting level of these sexual functions varies with the individual of course.

Finally, here are some suggestions on strengthening the kidneys. Herman Aihara spoke often about the importance of maintaining kidney strength. In TCM, the kidneys are thought to the "battery pack" or "power station" for all the body's energy needs. Many years of experience have demonstrated to me the importance of safeguarding the strength of the kidneys for the sake of healing power, immune system strength, and overall health and vitality.

To Strengthen the Kidneys

• Use a high quality sea salt such as Celtic Sea Salt or Si Salt. Regulate salt intake. Salt needs are individual. If something tastes salty it is too salty. If something tastes bland it is not salty enough.

Cook salt into food, don't add at the table.

- Avoid dry, hard, crispy (salty) snack foods like chips, crackers, popcorn, and too much bread. (Remember, the stomach must turn all food into a soup-like mixture.)
- Walk—especially outdoors and uphill, walk barefoot on morning dew.
- Breathe fresh air.
- Do something to sweat—gardening, house cleaning, manual labor, aerobic exercise, or sauna (far infrared).
- Take warm salt baths—2 cups of inexpensive salt in a tub of warm water. Soak for 10-20 minutes.
- Practice core strengthening/trunk rotating exercises—Pilates, Yoga, Tai Qi, Qi Gong.
- Massage (rub Tiger Balm into) the kidney source point on the sole of the foot (midway side to side and 1/3 down from toes to heel).
- Rest/nap in the late afternoon (3:00 to 5:00 p.m.).
- Avoid caffeine and sugar.
- Apply ginger compress (or hot water bottle or heating pad) over mid/low back especially in late afternoon or evening. Before bed is a good time.

And Beyond

Specific healthy dietary and physical practices are necessary to maintain healing power, a strong immune system, and overall health; however, other energies that make up our whole being must be addressed as well for true healing, vital health, and a strong immune system.

The next chapter examines the energetic dimension, particularly, how mental, emotional, and spiritual attitudes impact health, healing power, and the immune system.

Chapter 12

Energetic Healing Power

A strong immune system requires an integration of the physical and energetic dimensions of life.

In Chapter 11, the focus was primarily on diet and other physical practices of healing power like strengthening the kidneys and immune system. This chapter examines the energetic dimension of healing power and strengthening the immune system—the mental, emotional, and spiritual aspects of life. Here is a quote from *Healing with Whole Foods, 3rd edition*, by Paul Pitchford:

"The single most important principle for strengthening immunity is an attitude of nonseparation in one's personal life...When separation is felt between people, it is often because of unresolved emotional issues. This can be changed through sincere forgiveness followed by unconditional gratitude for everything that happens and has happened. According to traditional Chinese physiology, getting rid of old resentments clears the liver of obstructions, which in turn permits the smooth and vigorous circulation of protective and other qi energies. The cliché that we hurt only ourselves with anger is in fact a physiological truth. Once the work of resolving resentments in underway, the choices for diet and lifestyle factors should fall into place. Without this work, one tends to eat and live in ways that support the old, unresolved patterns." (p. 87)

Constraint and Flow

Circulation is one of the most important aspects of health and healing as presented in Chapter 11. Good circulation bears blood, nutrients, micronutrients, and energy (life force) to the cells and transports the byproducts of cell activity away from the cells for elimination. Smooth and unimpeded circulation strengthens healing power and the immune system. Here, circulation is a central idea as well, only now it is specifically applied to the circulation of energy (life force).

The concept of *constraint and flow* allows us to understand the workings of the immune system from the perspective of energy circulation. Constraint can be anything physical, mental, emotional, or spiritual that is moving too slowly or is completely blocked.

How is constraint experienced? If one tries or desires to do, say, think, feel, be, go toward, move, change, or express *anything* and feels impeded, blocked, frustrated, diminished, or depleted in any way, that is *constraint.* Energy constraint can come from mental rigidity and arrogance, emotional resentments and disappointments, and/or spiritual conflicts. Examples are anger at some perceived injustice, holding grudges, insufficient emotional and/or physical affection, paralyzing fears, doubts, worries, tightness with money, emotional clutter and confusion, and questioning of spiritual beliefs.

Many, if not all of us, have experienced these kinds of energetic constraints. Such constraints prevent the free flow of energy and blood. In this way, constraint that has an energetic origin can eventually become physically depleting and lead to pain, organ dysfunction, and the "10,000 diseases" sages cite. Constraint takes us out of the harmonious flow of energy in body, mind, and/or spirit and weakens the healing power of the immune system leading to inconvenient or uncomfortable results. If constructively interpreted, such experiences can be understood as an alert that we are out of balance—information, if acted upon, that can save us considerable suffering.

Conversely, *flow* is the free, harmonious, balanced transformation of energy and blood. In contrast to constraint, flow is characterized by change, transition, transformation, flexibility, adaptability, fluidity, forgiveness, and gratitude. Choosing options that provide flow in life energy enable growth, development, and health leading to mental, emotional, and spiritual wellbeing. A constant state of flow may not be possible in the dualistic physical dimension; however, we can get better at it in the energetic dimension, experiencing flow to a greater degree, more frequently, and for longer periods of time. The process of creating flow is discussed in greater detail later in this chapter.

Decision Making

Decision making is helpful in understanding the role of constraint and flow with regard to energetic health. We live in a relative, dualistic world. A concept of analysis like yin and yang is an example of our perception of duality. All experiences we encounter in the physical world are dualistic—a front and a back, an up and down, right and left, hot and cold. When making any decision, distill the complexity of choices down to an "A" or "B" choice—just two choices. If you reflect and think about "A" and "B" carefully, one of them will feel like constraint, one will feel like flow. The difference between "A" and "B" may be almost imperceptible but there will be a difference. Nothing in the relative world is exactly 50/50, just like yin and yang; there is always a preponderance of one or the other. This preponderance of constraint and flow can be recognized between any two choices. One option will have even the slightest edge of flow energy. Even if the flow option flies in the face of practicality, acceptability, or ego desire, have the courage to follow the energetic truth that the flow option is the healthier choice. Much pain and suffering can be avoided in this way.

Personal Truth and George Ohsawa

Identifying the deeper truth and reality of a situation relieves energetic constraint and promotes flow. Indeed, the reluctance to acknowledge the truth of a matter is the most profound form of constraint. It literally chokes and even blocks the flow of energy and blood. Truth here is one's personal truth—what each of us knows in our heart to be true and right, as long as it doesn't harm others of course. It may not make sense to anyone else, but it doesn't have to, it is a truth that is personal and unique. I believe we ignore, deny, or deflect our truth at our peril. To deny one's truth is to constrain life force. And to knowingly constrain life force will give rise to the "10,000 diseases." This is an energetic view of health.

Furthermore, acknowledging personal truth is a way of communing with divine energy. When we connect with divine energy we feel whole; we know our purpose in this life; we know we are on the path of our true destiny. Choices that align with divine energy take the form of something we simply "can't not do."

Framing a choice as something we "can't not do" is stronger than viewing a choice as something we "must do." "Must do" implies some form of coercion or obligation—a choice we might resist, regret, and later attempt to change. "Can't not do" is utterly disarming and compelling. After much study, experience, and reflection, when we submit to the truth of a choice that we "can't not do," our conscience is clear and our minds and spirit are free. All comes to good because our decision is derived from that which continually creates life—life force, divine energy. This is flow. Strong healing power and a strong immune system are side effects to this larger spiritual connection.

To my understanding, it is this kind of freedom that George Ohsawa was so intent on teaching to the world. Listening to Herman Aihara talk about his time with Ohsawa, what most impressed me was that Ohsawa taught people how to think, to develop good judgment. Ohsawa would lecture, pose questions to his students, and would reward the response that came from individual original thinking. Even as Ohsawa taught the order of the universe, he charged each student to "see for yourself." To me, this is another way of talking about personal truth. See for yourself! What makes sense to you? Discover what you "can't not do" in life.

Personal and Clinical Examples

About 25 years ago when I was working at the George Ohsawa Macrobiotic Foundation in California, I received a business proposition that would have required me to move to the Midwest. On the face of it, the proposition was appealing, but I had reservations. I continued to override those reservations as the constraint around the project mounted. A week before I was to move, I was surrounded by all my packed belongings in my apartment when I discovered that I was laying flat on my back on the living room floor.. I couldn't move. Gravity (energy) was pinning me to the floor. I overrode that piece of information and continued with preparations to move. Three days later the engine in my car blew up. It would take three weeks to repair. Then, I finally got it. I called the person who made the offer and told him I couldn't come. Interestingly, when I finally "got it," I felt so light and relieved, like this had been the correct decision all along. It had just taken a little suffering to discover it.

Clinically, there are two examples of constraint that I often encounter. One is the reluctance to speak up that often correlates with migraine headaches, thyroid issues, and heart and respiratory problems. This person continually stuffs her/his true feelings and thoughts creating a pressure cooker of resentment. Then one day, one of the above symptoms mysteriously and inexplicably appears.

Another example, exclusively in men, is prostate issues. I've worked with many prostate cancer cases over the years. In every case that I have encountered, the patient remarked about physical intimacy frustration. This is not to say that all men who experience intimacy frustration have prostate issues, but I have not seen a case of medically diagnosed prostate problems that did not have intimacy frustration as an accompanying experience.

Engendering Flow—Stage 1: Recognition

There are three stages or processes that have been helpful in reducing the constraint and restoring the flow of energy—the flow of life and vitality. The first stage is recognition that constraint exists. This usually entails becoming aware of a long-practiced pattern of relating to the world. For example, I see many patients who report being harshly criticized as children, usually by a well-meaning but overbearing parent. Since virtually all children seek to please and gain approval from parents, enduring criticism and striving to remove that criticism becomes a motivation for many decisions. This need for approval can set up a similar pattern in adult situations and relationships.

A patient, call her Jane, came in one day without any particular physical issue. Jane was actually quite healthy, fit, and athletic; however, emotionally she was a wreck. Her chief concern was that she was sad much of the time and prone to sudden bouts of weeping. Jane's partner had verbally abused her for a number of years; specifically, that she was intellectually inferior because Jane only had a master's degree and her partner had a Ph.D. Eventually, both she and her partner acted out their frustrations and the relationship came to an end. Further investigation revealed that Jane had been involved in two other relationships with similar outcomes. The deeper truth that had eluded her was that she had been trained by her mother to be a pleaser when she was growing up and had not been given encouragement or praise as a teenager. Jane reported numerous instances from her childhood and adolescence when her mother had criticized her with opinionated verbal abuse such as, "Wearing sporty clothes make you look plain, why don't you wear more attractive girl clothes." As an adult then, Jane accepted verbally abusive behavior as normal, even as an expression of love. When she recognized that this pattern of verbal abuse was a constraint in her life, she was on her way to healing.

Engendering Flow—Stage 2: Validate

After a constraining pattern is recognized, the second stage is to garner the honesty to validate these perceptions. I have seen many people recognize a pattern of constraint only to trot out a sophisticated stream of rationales why the pattern can't or shouldn't be changed. Denial, deflection, and defensiveness are the adversaries of honesty. Interestingly, I find that the more intelligent someone is, the more clever the denials and deflections. And truly, the only way to transcend such rationales is to unwaveringly focus on one's personal truth in a situation. Cleverness, denial, and illusion always and eventually yield to one's personal truth. Such truth, unique for each of us, is the direct connection to the divine that we all are capable of knowing. It is, in macrobiotic terms, the order of the universe.

Following the example above, when Jane honestly validated to herself that her partner's/mother's verbal abuse was opinion and not her own personal truth, she understood, for the first time, that her own personal truth was more important than their opinion. This validation was an essential second stage in transforming constraint into flow for Jane.

Engendering Flow—Stage 3: Take Action

The third stage is likely the most difficult for most people, but also the most healing. After recognition and honest validation of constraint, it is time to take action. This is the time when one's longest held, deepest, and most upsetting fears will emerge. The function of fears is to prevent us from making change. We avoid change; we much prefer status quo. Change means we will have to give up something, but it also means that we get or create something new. Constant change in the physical world is the one reality on which we might all agree. To change is to mirror the order of the universe, to align ourselves with Qi, Prana, Life Force...that energy that only knows creation, always transforming, always moving, and always growing, always evolving, whether it is the workings of a single cell, our consciousness, or the chemical transformations in a distant star.

Taking action means we must confront our fears and move through them. To allow fears to inhibit is to enable constraint. To push through fears guided by one's personal truth creates flow. Then, we have the opportunity to reinvent ourselves with our own true, unique vision. Such change is beyond exhilarating. It is, in a spiritual sense, to know divine energy. In those moments of conscious true change we transcend the duality of the physical world and experience the oneness of all things, our personal energy streams unimpeded in consonance with Qi, Prana, Divine Energy—the order of the universe.

In the example of Jane, she had to speak up to opinionated criticism. It meant changing the dynamics of a primary relationship. It meant saying to her partner that she would no longer accept the opinion that she was somehow inferior. It meant saying to her mother that, while she respected her views, her personal truth was different. Jane bravely faced the prospect of disapproval, or withdrawal of love, for the sake of living her personal truth. Indeed, she and her partner split up, but the relationship with her mother survived. As she reported these conversations, her face relaxed and she sat up straighter.

Attachment and Will

I attribute the following thought to Buddhism, "Attachment is the source of all suffering." Taking action may mean that a long-standing situation will change. Anyone who has been in a long-term relationship knows how intertwined a relationship becomes and how daunting and fearful it is to change or dissolve that relationship; but, if that is where the truth of the matter takes you, then you can't not make the change. To knowingly continue to endure constraint may set the stage for the "10,000 diseases."

When you take action, you must exercise non-attachment. Release attachment to the consequences of your action. You must believe that action taken in truth and honesty will ultimately come to good because such change reflects and comes from the order of the universe and from the Qi, Prana, Divine Energy that animates all life.

Everything turns on the exercise of will; at some point we must make a decision to act. Change doesn't just happen; we must initiate it in our own unique vision, our personal truth. This requires clarity, courage, and force of will.

Take Heart

This is heavy stuff, but it only appears so because the action finally taken is redressing many years of accumulated constraint. As this process is integrated into how one relates to life and spirit, it becomes less disruptive and tumultuous. Integrating the energetic and physical dimensions of life is an effective way to strengthen the immune system and pave the way for health, wellbeing, and fulfillment.

Chapter 13

Managing Fight or Flight

"Fight or flight" is a reflex response by the body's systems to threat. Way back in human history that amounted to threat of physical harm. "Fight or flight" rapidly engaged certain body functions to help escape that threat. This is the original function of "fight or flight." Nowadays, everything from a horn honking to being called into the boss's office to watching a violent movie triggers similar bodily functions. These days we know it by the familiar label of "stress."

Definitions

A dictionary definition of stress is: 1. Pressure or tension exerted on a material object; or more to the point here, 2. A state of mental or emotional strain or tension resulting from adverse or very demanding circumstances. Some synonyms for stress are strain, pressure, nervous tension, worry, anxiety, trouble, difficulty.

Here are some other definitions and results of stress from my own thinking:

• Anything you feel pressure to do that you don't want to do.
• Anything you can't transform back to equilibrium—too fast, too loud, too extreme (conflict, emotion, etc.) that overwhelms you.
• Stress changes *order* (from knowing who, where, what you are) into chaos (can't make sense of anything).
• Stress is being overly attached to ___________ (fill in the blank…anything).
• Stress is ego run amuck—"I want this, I want that, or any would'a, should'a, could'a."

- Stress produces an acidic condition.
- Stress leads to all kinds of inflammation.

Pause for a moment and think about your own definition of stress. Can you think of a specific event, situation, person, or emotion that you experienced as stress? Is it an event from your childhood? Is it an irritating personality trait of your spouse? Is it the annoying behavior of your overbearing boss? Driving in congested traffic? How does it feel? Do you feel a physical sensation anywhere in your body? Can you put an emotional label on it?

Not All Bad

Not all stress is destructive. Stress can help you stay focused, energetic, and alert. In emergency situations, your response to stress can save your life. Your physiological response to stress activates the body's defenses in a rapid, automatic process giving you extra strength to defend yourself; for example, slamming on the brakes (without thinking) to avoid an accident—a "fight-or-flight" reaction. The stress response also helps you rise to meet challenges. Stress is what keeps you on your toes, sharpens your concentration, drives you to perform work or study, or helps you physically respond to danger—real or imagined. But beyond a certain point, stress stops being helpful and can cause major damage to your health, your mood, your productivity, your relationships, and your quality of life. See: *http://www.helpguide.org/articles/stress/stress-symptoms-causes-and-effects.htm*

Physiology of Stress—The Evolutionary Design

The experience of stress (real or imagined) releases cortisol, the "fight or flight" hormone. Fear increases cortisol.

Imagine you are a prehistoric person out on the savannah foraging for roots or berries and you come upon a saber-tooth tiger. The "fight or flight" response (in this example, likely flight is the wiser choice) releases cortisol in your body which quickens your heart rate and respiration, elevates your blood pressure, inhibits the glucose storage function (in the liver) of insulin (but not insulin's function of transporting glucose into the cells) keeping a plentiful amount glucose in the blood, sharpens your mind and senses, and shuts down any unnecessary function to enable you to focus all your energy on escaping being eaten by the saber-tooth tiger. Without thinking, your reaction is to run to the nearest tree and climb high up to safety. This is "flight" to save your life.

Once you had gotten to safety and the saber-tooth tiger wanders off, you would have successfully addressed and resolved that stressful situation and hormone levels would return to normal. That's how our stress response, "fight or flight" is designed to protect us.

Nowadays, most of us are not confronted with life threatening saber tooth tigers. Fortunately, most of us rarely encounter a serious threat to our physical wellbeing. However, it doesn't take an imminent physical threat to trigger the stress response and the accompanying release of cortisol. In the modern world stress factors that can trigger "fight or flight" are everywhere, all the time. Stress is nearly inescapable and can easily become chronic. Here are some examples:

External sources of stress

- Health challenge or accident
- Work or school
- Relationship difficulties
- Financial problems
- Being too busy
- Children and family

Internal causes of stress

- Chronic worry
- Pessimism
- Negative self-talk
- Unrealistic expectations/perfectionism
- Rigid thinking, lack of flexibility
- All-or-nothing attitude

Long-term effects of chronic stress

If stress is short-lived, infrequent, or better yet, if you have developed successful strategies for managing stress, the effects on your health are minimal, perhaps even negligible. If you had a happy childhood without any major physical or emotional trauma, you probably didn't experience any serious effects of stress as a child. How many of us can say that? Far more common is one or more physical or emotional traumas in childhood. Stress these days is neither infrequent nor short-lived and most people don't develop successful strategies for managing stress. Relentless and overwhelming stress, sadly, is more the norm today than the exception. Here are some long-term effects of chronic stress:

1. Chronic blood sugar imbalances can lead to Type 2 diabetes—too much glucose and ineffective insulin.

2. Weight gain—cortisol moves triglycerides from storage to visceral fats (deep in the abdomen).

3. High glucose/low insulin effectiveness starves cells, triggers appetite, and can lead to overeating.

4. Immune system suppression—cortisol checks inflammation and chronic inflammation (from poor diet and stress) keeps cortisol high. Your immune system then is always responding on high ("fight or flight"). Eventually your immune system gets exhausted leading to increased susceptibility to colds, food allergies, gastro-intestinal issues, cancer, and autoimmune disorders.

5. Gastro-intestinal problems—digestion/assimilation occurs best in a peaceful state (parasympathetic nervous system—"rest and digest"). Cortisol excites the nervous system (sympathetic nervous system—"fight or flight"). So, eating in a stressful state compromises digestion/absorption, indigestion ensues, and the mucosal lining of the gastro-intestinal tract becomes irritated and inflamed, possibly leading to ulcers, irritable bowel syndrome, and/or colitis.

6. Cardiovascular Disease—arterial constriction and increased blood pressure can lead to vessel damage and plaque buildup resulting in increased risk of heart attack. Type A personalities (go all the time) have a higher risk of heart disease than type B personalities

(more relaxed).

7. Fertility issues—disruption of menstrual cycle, erectile dysfunction, hampered production of sex hormones.

8. Other effects—insomnia, chronic fatigue, thyroid disorders, depression, dementia.

Overwhelming and Paralyzing

When stress overwhelms you, it can be paralyzing. You are unable to transform stress back into equilibrium and you can feel stuck—powerless to change. In that powerless state you may succumb to strain, pressure, worry, or anxiety—that "stressed out" feeling. You want to curl up in a ball on your bed and shut the world out. The pint of Häagen-Dazs in the freezer beckons with the promise of stress-obliterating sensual pleasure. But that pleasure is only temporary. As soon as you're finished eating the ice cream the pleasure is gone, the stress is still there, and your body has a pint of Häagen-Dazs ice cream to deal with. There are other ways to transform stress.

The Sphere Analogy

Take a look at the following diagram:

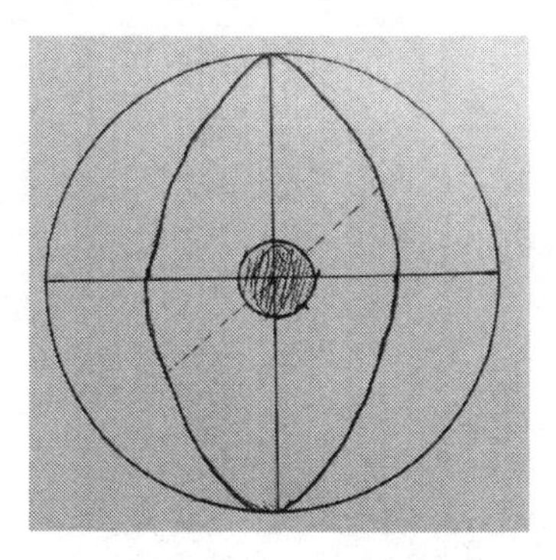

It is a three dimensional sphere with an x-axis and y-axis (solid lines) and a z-axis (dotted line). The outer lines or surface of the sphere represent all of the situations, people, relationships, emotions, energies, or events that can pull or push you out of equilibrium. The smaller darkened sphere in the center represents the space or energy where you have effectively transformed stress into equilibrium. In that space your condition is neither too high nor too low, forward nor backward, fast nor slow. It is a safe, secure place for body, mind, and spirit that you can inhabit if you are able to manage and transform stress to equilibrium.

Transforming Stress Into Equilibrium - General Strategy

The fundamental, most basic, essential, crucial element for managing stress is to remember...*You have a choice!* Choice gives you the power to transform. Choice gives you the power to change. Choice gives you the power to create the life you envision. Never forget that. Remind yourself every morning when you wake up and every night before you go to sleep. The first step in transforming stress into equilibrium is to stabilize your physiology. If you are able to stabilize your physiology, you have the opportunity to advance further in transforming stress back to equilibrium. While it is absolutely necessary to stabilize your physiology, that alone is not sufficient to transform stress. More steps are required.

Stabilize Your Physiology

Emphasize primarily whole/natural plant-based foods (some animal foods may be helpful for some conditions) such as a macrobiotic diet.

- Include probiotic foods—fermented foods like miso, pickles, sauerkraut.
- Reduce/eliminate refined sugar and refined carbohydrates.
- Reduce/eliminate all processed/refined food.
- Reduce/eliminate caffeine.
- Reduce/eliminate alcohol.
- Reduce/eliminate hard, dry, crispy, salty foods.
- Be careful with all salt—it raises cortisol.
- Practice regular, moderate, appropriate exercise—light aerobic exercise combined with some kind of stretching (Yoga, Tai Qi, Qi Gong).
- Get adequate rest.

• Attend to emotional maintenance—learn to nurture, forgive, and be kind and generous to your self.

Step by Step Transformation of Stress

1. Learn to recognize stress before it gets out of control.
2. Once you recognize it, remember that *you have a choice* of how to interpret/relate to stress and then-
3. STOP—Intervene in your experience of stress by-
4. Taking a single conscious breath (doesn't even have to be deep) and pausing to-
5. Reflect, so that you have the opportunity to bring-
6. Mindfulness to your experience of stress and then you can-
7. Clearly see the choice you are about to make and choose to make a new one and then-
8. Stress will dissipate.

How to Manage Stress - Specific Actions/Strategies

1. Consciously express gratitude for all the abundance and comforts you enjoy. We really require very little in this life. As the Chinese proverb says—"Food on the table, roof over our heads, already in Paradise." Expressing gratitude can lift you above the pressures and strain of stress and bring you peace.
2. Use meditation/prayer as forms of gratitude and maintaining mindfulness (an essential quality for transforming stress).
3. Practice saying "no" to pressures, requests.
4. Limit screen time.
5. Take a break from social media and the news.
6. Dim the lights.
7. Reduce exposure to violent images and upsetting or extreme energies.
8. Listen to relaxing music.
9. Take warm baths.
10. Massage your feet.
11. Engage in sensual touching with your partner, including sex.
12. Make use of essential oils—I like lavender.

13. Get outside yourself—giving and service; volunteer, helping of any kind.

14. Cry/sigh/moan—just let it out. Tears of elimination (not rumination) lighten one's load.

15. Do something fun, entertaining, outside the ordinary.

16. Mundane life activities can calm and distract the stressed and agitated mind. All of these help to restore order:

a. Make a healthy, nutritious, delicious meal.
b. Clean anything.
c. Wash dishes.
d. Do laundry.
e. Repair something, especially if it is simple and has been broken a long time.
f. Tidy up your desk or closet.
g. Make your bed.
h. Take a shower, shave, spruce yourself up.
i. Changes clothes—dress up/down.
j. Nap, sleep, go to bed early.
k. Sing at the top of your lungs (in your car to your favorite song works nicely).
l. Gaze at the horizon—look out on an ocean horizon or mountain panorama (photo will do in a pinch) and just gaze for long moments. Allow yourself to be mesmerized by the setting and just relax.

Conclusion

None of us can escape stress. Stress is everywhere and all the time in today's modern world. However, we can learn to manage and transform stress back to equilibrium. Be patient with yourself and learn how to transform stress and persevere. Likely you will run up against long-held and deeply ingrained patterns of responding to your experiences of life. Pick one specific incident of stress and work on just that. Apply some of the suggestions contained in this chapter, generate your own, and do more research to find out what can be helpful for you.

Part 4

The Culture of Macrobiotics

Chapter 14

Community Building

Beyond the applications of macrobiotic theory and practice for personal health and wellbeing over the years, one of the most lasting and positive contributions of macrobiotics has been the establishing and sustaining of community activities and organizations.

Macrobiotic education centers like the Kushi Institute have, for over 40 years, provided education services and a place for people from around the world to attend and learn the theory and skills of a macrobiotic diet and lifestyle and to meet and get to know other like-minded individuals.

Macrobiotic summer camps are a tradition started by George Ohsawa in 1960. Ohsawa's camps were Spartan affairs in nature with tent camping and outdoor cooking. That tradition has continued up to the present in the form of the French Meadows Summer Camp started by Herman Aihara and his associates in 1970. The Kushi Summer Conference has been held on the East Coast since 1978 with less rustic accommodations. Today, in addition to summer and winter conferences, cruises provide an opportunity for those interested in macrobiotics to gather. All of these events feature lectures, cooking classes, exercise classes, counseling services, and provide rallying points for those interested and dedicated to learning and practicing macrobiotics.

In the early days of macrobiotic activities, many teachers would travel extensively to teach and counsel. Back in the 1970s, I've heard it said that someone could travel almost anywhere in the United States and find a friendly macrobiotic center, household, or individual where one could get a meal and have a place to sleep.

In those days, there were many macrobiotic centers in many American cities with ongoing education activities, cooking classes, dinners, potlucks, and lectures. In addition, macrobiotic centers and individuals published magazines, journals, and books to inform, grow, and knit the macrobiotic community together.

Macrobiotics emphasizes eating a healthy diet. It is thought that a healthy diet will produce healthy blood, and healthy blood can positively influence consciousness. Herman Aihara taught that eating together as a couple, family, or community would promote good communication because in eating the same healthy foods, persons would create a similar quality of blood leading to harmonious vibrations among those sharing meals together.

Creating a strong empathetic harmonious atmosphere among macrobiotic practitioners has been one of the most remarkable influences of macrobiotic theory and practice. Humans are humans and differences invariably arise, but to anyone who has been to any of the above events or read and followed macrobiotics over the years, there is an undeniable sense of calm and peacefulness that permeates macrobiotic people and activities. One of Michio Kushi's stated dreams/goals was to promote one peaceful world.

From my personal experience over many years, I find the cohesion that macrobiotic food and practices promote is palpable. In my many years of interest and direct involvement with macrobiotics, I can unequivocally say that I have met many high-quality individuals. The macrobiotic folks that I know are some of the kindest, most genuine, heart-centered people I have met in this lifetime. I have made dear friends that have remained friends these many years later. Each time I attend a camp or a conference it is like returning home. For me anyway, no group of people is more comfortable to be with.

Chapter 15

Biases and Blind Spots

We are all human. Both individuals and organizations have specific viewpoints, peculiarities, biases, and prejudices. For macrobiotics to remain vital, biases and blind spots must be identified, discussed, and modified. What follows are my thoughts on practices that have limited macrobiotic popularity and development.

Authoritarian Behavior

In Chapter 4, I presented a few ideas why I believe macrobiotics is not a medical modality. In an environment where failures and inconsistencies are ignored and dissent results in ostracism, there is a possibility of creating unquestioned authority figures—teachers or counselors whose word is accepted on faith rather than through critical thinking. In attempting to defend a confusing theoretical structure, this kind of rigid authoritarian behavior can easily arise. And so it has in the development of macrobiotics.

It's unfortunate that in public discourse often the person who can speak the loudest and longest, or argue most skillfully will carry the day. Often such a person strays from the truth; certain politicians come to mind. A perfect set of circumstances in the development of macrobiotics allowed for this type of persuasion to proliferate, starting with a theory, philosophy, and practice that is foreign—macrobiotics came from Asia, specifically Japan. Macrobiotic teachings, books, and classes are filled with foreign sounding words, strange food names, and a unique philosophical focus. Most people who come to macrobiotics don't have sufficient background to evaluate what is being said because they don't know enough about the basic ideas, be they cultural or linguistic. Indeed, all of this often comes off as exotic, mysterious, and alluring.

The teacher/counselor then appears to be the one in possession of "secrets" that he/she will dole out to the students in such a way as to set him- or herself up as a controlling power figure. I believe much of this took place unconsciously. Combine strange sounding ideas, a teacher who is perhaps not solid on the ideas, and an inconsistent theory and the whole presentation is on shaky ground. To preserve an image of authority, the teacher often pulls rank. Wanting to please the teacher, like we all do, students acquiesce and go away scratching their heads not quite convinced by the answer.

Fear Mongering and God-Complex

Another bias that creeps into macrobiotics is fear mongering to persuade or to quiet dissent. Fear mongering is seemingly an inextricable component of macrobiotic culture. Many macrobiotic events include comments about "cheating" and the guilt, self-recrimination, and judgment that accompany it. Fear mongering extends to attempting to make macrobiotic theory and practice a medical modality. Having someone shake his or her finger at you for eating a chocolate chip cookie saying that it will give you cancer is fear mongering at its most egregious, unfounded causation masquerading as a judgment and condemnation. The sick, weak, and confused don't have the mental clarity or the gumption to challenge such specious reasoning. I remember hearing a theory that a prominent macrobiotic teacher developed ovarian cancer because she was fond of eating the crusty chewy bottom rice from pressure cooked brown rice. It sounds ridiculous now, but I remember seeing people nodding their heads in agreement.

God-complex and fear mongering dovetail with Judeo-Christian dogma and tradition of sin, guilt, punishment, and the judgment of a wrathful god. Instead of Judeo-Christian dogma, substitute macrobiotic dogma with a ready-made means to influence people and control the culture. People don't dare think on their own. "What if I am wrong? I could get cancer. I better believe and do what the counselor says. Then I'll be okay."

God-complex and fear mongering are the antithesis of the vision of macrobiotics as a means to experience freedom. Each individual trying to see for him- or herself if something is effective is a central philosophical tenet of macrobiotics. When that is ignored or taken away, it's very difficult for someone to create vibrant health and to realize his or her dream. How can anyone face the challenges of life if he or she is afraid to make a decision that disagrees with what some authority figure has previously told them?

The moment of personal decision is precisely the time to make a unique personal departure toward one's individual path in life. To think for oneself is the only way to realize one's purpose, one's true destiny, one's true fate. True destiny holds fulfillment of life experience. If the tools to realize that fulfillment are undermined or taken away, someone is left to wander through life in confusion, frustration, and disappointment.

Fear and Diet

Macrobiotic fear mongering is most prevalent in dietary recommendations by counselors. I agree that a consistent unhealthy dietary pattern over a long period of time is likely to contribute to the development of a pathological condition but, to tell someone he or she developed cancer because of one particular food, is irresponsible and unbelievable. Only to someone who is willing to accept such a thing on blind faith does this make sense. Many people have come to me as acupuncture patients filled with fear about their dietary choices—fears that were impressed upon them from macrobiotic books, teachers, and counselors. They had been frightened into believing that the only way they could experience health was by adhering to the counselor's prescriptions for their dietary practice. One patient, a woman age 72, became anxious and was nearly in tears describing how she felt she had to prepare a full macrobiotic banquet for her and her husband daily, petrified of making any personal modifications or they would get sicker.

The comment that always catches my attention is, "Oh, that's not macrobiotic." I think that phrase captures the disempowerment that seems to infect many macrobiotic students. It implies that there is a linear absolute standard that can be generally applied to everyone in all circumstances. That's not Big Life. That's disempowerment. Macrobiotic students often become so frightened that they cannot allow themselves to make a free personal decision. Whatever they choose, they feel they have to square it with what the teacher or the book says. As such, they can't try and see. They repeat the rigid dogma they were given.

My vision is that the mission of macrobiotics is to provide people with information and skills, and then guide and teach them how to make creative decisions to realize their own unique personal dreams, be they physical health, career, or social relationships.

Counselor Training

A counselor (or teacher) who is well-trained in disciplines in addition to macrobiotics whether it's TCM, Ayurvedic, Western Medicine, or Naturopathy, can bring the knowledge, skills, and perspective of those modalities to macrobiotics and better translate macrobiotic theory and practice into effective tools for supporting health and wellbeing.

It takes emotional and spiritual maturity on the part of a teacher and counselor to be able to successfully teach macrobiotics and that has been lacking among macrobiotic leaders. Over the years in a variety of situations, I have detected a kind of glee among macrobiotic leaders in the failure of other teachers, counselors, and centers. What results is political bickering and defensive turf wars rather than cooperation.

The god-like self-importance, self-righteous fear mongering mentality may be one reason that macrobiotic counselors charge egregiously high fees. I mean $500 for one hour of someone's time? I feel embarrassed that someone would charge that much for a consultation. It's no wonder that there's very little follow-up business and that macrobiotic counselors struggle to make a living.

Furthermore, charging so much for a consultation is problematic in several ways:

• It is a huge financial burden on the client, many of whom are sick, weak, confused, and desperate.
• It implies a life or death significance to the pronouncements of the counselor and contributes to the god-like aura of the counselor. "If it costs so much, I had better do what I am told to the letter or I would've wasted my money, and I'll end up sick(er)."
• It limits the availability of counseling primarily to the wealthy.
• The high fee intimidates the client and sets up a power-over-weakness dynamic that significantly disempowers the client.
• Clients who pay a high consultation fee and come away confused, intimidated, and overwhelmed are unlikely to return to that service or recommend it to someone else.

To my knowledge, there has never been the development of a macrobiotic treatment protocol that could be used for ongoing health maintenance. The lack of a reliable treatment modality comprising differential diagnoses and specific treatment plans severely limits the development of macrobiotics as an ongoing counseling practice. Also, the absence of a compiled body of diagnosis and treatment histories for evaluating the effectiveness of methods and recommendations may lead counselors to repeat ineffective methods.

What developed in this environment of god-like bias and fear mongering is for macrobiotic teachers/counselors (perhaps unconsciously) to set themselves up as imperious unquestioned authority figures. He (mostly), but she as well, becomes someone who has all the answers, is (nearly) always right, and is duty-bound to preserve the purity of the dogma, set the heretics straight, or boot them out altogether, and to blame the client for his or her lack of success.

Thoughtful, creative investigation and critique is not and cannot be tolerated and a cult-like organization of unquestioned leaders and unquestioning followers emerges. Macrobiotic teachers and counselors, quite unintentionally perhaps, preyed upon the weak, sick, and lost. A kind of codependence developed in which the leaders were always consolidating and preserving their power, and followers were disempowered and walked away confused, frustrated and disappointed.

I encourage all macrobiotic practitioners to seek teachers and counselors who avoid fear mongering and who are also well-trained in complementary disciplines. Some macrobiotic counselors and teachers have widened their views over the years, but there is still much to do to make macrobiotic teachings more accessible throughout the world.

Chapter 16

Coloring Outside the Lines

This chapter highlights some of the habits and attitudes around the macrobiotic community for many years that I believe have set an unhealthy example and have had unhealthy outcomes. Some of these practices are rooted in cultural and generational matters.

I don't intend to accuse any one in particular or to judge any one person's behavior. Each of us has a unique view and experience of life and one's personal choices are one's personal business. What follows are practices that do not contribute to health and wellbeing and are best omitted from a macrobiotic lifestyle.

Tobacco, Alcohol, And Caffeine

Stretching back to the earliest years of macrobiotics, tobacco, alcohol, and caffeine were consumed by many of the leaders of macrobiotics. George Ohsawa set the example. He smoked cigarettes and a pipe regularly and was fond of whiskey. I'm not sure if Ohsawa was much of a consumer of caffeine, but caffeine in the form of coffee did find its way into the practices of many early macrobiotic teachers. It's hard to believe in these times that the consumption of tobacco products could be considered healthy in any way. Despite the misdirection, misinformation, and downright subversion of information for many years by the tobacco industry on the health hazards of tobacco products, the health risks of consuming tobacco products are now nearly universally accepted. I remember reading or hearing of an attempt to justify smoking of tobacco by macrobiotic practitioners. It had something to do with the yang of the smoke balancing out the yin of the lungs. Today, any explanation that attempts to justify the consumption of tobacco products strains any kind of credibility to the breaking point.

What kind of message does it send and what kind of example does it set for a macrobiotic teacher to deliver a lecture on the benefits of macrobiotic practices then afterwards stepping outside to have a cigarette? I have seen videos and heard stories that some macrobiotic teachers would even smoke while teaching. Herman Aihara was honest about his days as a smoker. He was a student of Ohsawa and a Japanese man—features that would render someone inclined to become a smoker in his days. Herman freely admitted that he would smoke during his lectures in his early years of macrobiotic teaching in the United States. He said that the reason he quit was that he didn't want his daughter to take up the habit.

The Japanese Connection

I have lived in Japan three different times in my life. During these times I spent many hours socializing with Japanese people, particularly Japanese businessmen. Aggressively consuming alcohol and displaying public intoxication, at least at that time in the late 1970s to mid-1980s, were not only tolerated but considered something of a badge of achievement. Some of the attraction to alcohol among the Japanese is due to the social pressures that are present in their society. Japanese society is not unique in using alcohol to self-medicate to relieve pressures, but it is unique I believe in the social acceptance, encouragement, and nearly giddy embracing of aggressively pursuing alcohol intoxication.

Using the macrobiotic energetic formulations, alcohol and salt are opposites. Also, sugar and salt are opposites. It stands to reason that if people who consume a lot of salt and live in a salty place might develop an attraction to alcohol. Such are the conditions in Japan. The Japanese diet contains a lot of salt and Japan is an island country surrounded by a salty ocean. The macrobiotic recipes first brought to the United States had to be modified to accommodate the less salty-oriented palates of Americans, particularly those of European descent.

Japan is also like a very large small town in that it seems everybody knows everybody else's business. To be Japanese is to feel scrutinized, if not by a boss, teacher, or parent, then by the values of Japanese society in general. As such, most Japanese are under a lot of pressure. In a highly competitive society like Japan, to succeed takes dedicated, almost obsessive effort. Schoolchildren, even primary school age, go to extra classes and tutors after their regular school classes in hopes of gaining an edge on admission exams to the best universities. Another group in Japanese society that are often heavy drinkers are college students, almost as if it is the reward for all the years of studying so hard to get into a university.

Japanese men tend to be heavy consumers of alcohol and it seems to be a universal macho activity to drink large quantities of alcohol. That Ohsawa was fond of whiskey is not surprising. It would have been considered normal to drink alcohol (to excess) in those days and perhaps even now for someone who is a health care advocate or practitioner. I met a number of physicians when I lived in Japan and most of them had a fondness for alcohol. The same can be said for smoking among Japanese men. I imagine it was so common back in the 1940s and 1950s that it was considered normal. Before there was any public information about the hazards of smoking, I can see how it might have been considered normal and acceptable. I remember seeing ads in American magazines back in the 1960s in which doctors were promoting a particular brand of cigarette.

So, at least in part, with that social and cultural background, smoking and drinking alcohol made their way into the practices of macrobiotic leaders from Japan. The first generation of Ohsawa's macrobiotic students would have naturally imitated the habits of their teacher, especially since those habits were supported by the culture as well. So, that first generation of macrobiotic students brought those habits with them to the United States and wherever they traveled.

Coffee and Caffeine

There are many opinions about the effect and impact of caffeine.

I have read that caffeine is not injurious to health, and even that it is beneficial. I have also read articles describing the injurious effects of caffeine consumption. My professional focus is TCM (Traditional Chinese Medicine), and in TCM theory, the prolonged, regular consumption of caffeine is thought to be injurious to health.

Caffeine has no nutritional value. TCM theory teaches that caffeine has the capability of converting stored energy into active energy—like making a withdrawal from your savings account and not making a deposit. Everything is fine as long as there is a positive balance in your savings account. When your savings account becomes overdrawn, there is trouble. In TCM theory it's thought that caffeine converts reserve kidney energy into active energy. If that's done consistently over a long period of time, it will create a kidney deficiency. There are many sides to the debate about caffeine and I suppose it comes down to personal opinion; but, clinically I have yet to meet someone who could convince me that regular long-term caffeine consumption is a healthy practice. Just ask caffeine consumers what it is like when they try to stop. People experience headaches and fatigue.

There is a relationship between consuming coffee and cigarettes and drinking alcohol. Each of these substances has the power to change one's state of mind and being quickly and dramatically. As such, they can be used to alter or mask one's true energy state. For people who are under a lot of pressure to perform and know these substances can temporarily boost performance, they become nearly irresistible. The seduction of these substances lies in their ability to make one more (or different) than one is, at least temporarily.

It is my observation that these habits begin early in life often in an attempt to be or do more than one is capable of naturally. Competition can drive us to do unhealthy things. "If only I do just a little bit more of this I can get ahead, stay ahead, or be better enough to succeed in the way I hope," one might think. This is a compelling human desire. But once one starts down this road it is very difficult to turn back. So somewhere, even in the teenage years or early adulthood, one looks around for something to keep going, keep awake, or to give one that edge. Caffeine, often in the form of coffee, a highly desirable and socially acceptable beverage, can help provide that boost. And if one wants an additional energy boost and wants to look "cool," then there is the nicotine in cigarettes. People become revved up on caffeine and nicotine. How do they relax? Again, the desirable and socially acceptable means of relaxing, calming down, and relieving stress is to have a drink, an alcoholic drink at that. And after a few too many drinks, the desire to sober up or alleviate that hangover the next day sets in and caffeine in the form of coffee is attractive. Thus, a kind of balance is created, but a balance that encompasses wide swings of energy. Wide swings of energy from one extreme to another are depleting. Reserves invariably have to be called upon to restore balance after consuming caffeine, nicotine, or alcohol. Not right away, but eventually this consumption pattern contributes to the deterioration of overall health. The consumption of these substances by people in teaching and leadership positions does not set a healthy example.

Picking a Counselor

Occasionally after giving a lecture at a macrobiotic event, someone will approach me and ask how to select a counselor for a consultation. I rarely recommend a specific counselor. My response: take a good look at a prospective counselor and observe that person carefully. Try to set aside his/her name, reputation, high fee, and opinions you have heard from others. Honestly, clearly, without bias, look at his/her body and face, look into his/her eyes, listen to his/her voice, and observe his/her gestures. Does this person impress you as healthy? Do you want to be like this person? Because, if you follow his/her suggestions, most likely you will develop the same kind of energy. Possibly, if you follow his/her suggestions for some length of time, you may even begin to resemble this person.

It is fairly easy to repeat knowledge and ideas. It's quite another thing to actually walk the talk. In my experience, the mind, the mouth, and the words can effectively spin and obscure the truth. But the physiology never lies. You want to know which counselor is most appropriate for you? Look carefully at his/her physical presentation and you'll get an idea of what he/she is really like. And if you have developed your intuitive powers and have a strong sense of spirituality, when you look into his/her eyes you can see who he/she is. The eyes are often called the window to the soul. See what's in there. Look carefully, make clear observations, and trust your intuition, because some counselors are not healthy and do not set a healthy example. Don't be swayed by a high consultation fee. Paying a lot of money is no assurance of appropriateness or quality of service.

Women in Macrobiotics

Macrobiotics being derived from traditional Japanese or Asian diet and folkways carried with it some of the gender roles and gender attitudes from a previous era. Less so now I believe, but at the outset and for many years thereafter, women held a secondary position in macrobiotics. Men taught the theory classes and did the counseling and most of the writing. Women taught the cooking classes and took care of the kids. It's not an exaggeration to say that men made the decisions in the workplace and women were largely worker bees in the home or office.

Some years ago, I participated in a panel discussion at a macrobiotic conference. One of the panel members was talking about how people in macrobiotics tended to overwork. Someone in the room tried to make a point that women in macrobiotics were overworked, too. To which this particular panel member said, commenting upon his own situation, that his wife didn't work (outside the home he meant). I happen to know that his wife in addition to cooking and maintaining the household was homeschooling their children. What's that old saying? "Man may work from dawn till dusk but woman's work is never done." As old and as clichéd as this saying is, it pretty nearly summed up the role of women in the early days of macrobiotics. I bring this up to raise consciousness about women's place in macrobiotics so that any diminishment in the value of women's contributions doesn't continue in the future.

Chapter 17

A Swing and a Miss... or Two

Early on there was a near blind faith among macrobiotic adherents that diet could cure anything. Marriage not going so well? Just eat a macrobiotic diet. Having some financial difficulties? Practice a macrobiotic diet and lifestyle more carefully. This notion that a macrobiotic diet and lifestyle could solve anything might not have been explicitly stated, but it was implicitly communicated.

At the Vega Study Center in Oroville California there was a large wooden deck around the rear of the building. The wooden deck had dried out and needed to be re-sealed or refinished. The material used to finish and seal the wood was a toxic organic chemical, a varnish or some kind of solvent. The maintenance man at the time wore a respirator to apply this varnish and had to limit the amount of time he could work on the deck. Herman Aihara didn't believe that the respirator was necessary. To prove his point he volunteered to apply the varnish himself, without the use of a respirator. Several years later Herman died of congestive heart failure. I believe he died prematurely at age 77. It would be purely conjecture that the toxic exposure that he endured when applying that solvent or varnish contributed to his death, but what struck me was the macho arrogance that he exhibited daring to expose himself to a toxic chemical. I suspect that Herman felt that a macrobiotic diet made him invulnerable. To me, that appears foolish.

Emotional Health

One of the glaring omissions in macrobiotic theory and practice to this day is insufficient attention to emotional health in managing physical health. Early on, I guess that emotional issues were recognized as important, but the theory and practice of macrobiotics at the time didn't validate them as aspects that could influence physical health. As a result, many people with emotional issues did not have those issues addressed within a macrobiotic context.

Whether is was ignoring health risks, overwork, oppression, or heartbreak, some prominent macrobiotic teachers and counselors developed degenerative illness and passed away prematurely. Yet even today, macrobiotic theory and practice offers scant validation that emotions might influence physical health. My observation from many years of TCM practice is that emotional imbalances significantly contribute to the cause of many physical ailment manifestations.

Try It and See

Through the years there has been an under emphasis on George Ohsawa's teaching of "try it and see." "Try it and see" is central to empowerment of an individual. I would agree that, early on, one needs to have the structure of teachers, counselors, and books to learn the basic material and to provide guidance. And just as the mother bird knows when it is time to push the nestling out of the nest and force it to fly on its own, a good teacher or counselor knows when to guide the student into individual choice. Even, and especially, if that means that the student will make choices in opposition to what the teacher has taught or the counselor has advised. More on this topic may be found in Chapter 19.

Part 5

Good Judgment and Freedom

Chapter 18

Adaptability

One of the ideas prevalent in macrobiotics is that everything changes. In the material universe nothing stands still. Everyone and everything is constantly transforming and changing into someone or something else. In a constantly changing environment, adaptability is of utmost importance. If one cannot adapt, something will break from the pressure of unstoppable change. The principles of macrobiotics give one the tools for adaptability.

The dialectic is the principal tool for adaptability in macrobiotics. George Ohsawa says, "Civilized man has lost his dynamic adaptability, his key to infinite freedom." *Essential Ohsawa* p. 55. If one is locked into a rigid interpretation of any situation, options for transforming that situation are limited. Remember the example of 50° in Chapter 1 and what that means. If one's interpretation of 50° always means "cold," the range of decisions that one can make on a 50° day are limited. So, if it's mid-March, and the weather has been consistently below freezing and a 50° day comes along, one might decide that that's a good day to take a walk outside having been shut in all winter with cabin fever. On that mid-March day, 50° is probably going to feel warm. But, if 50° always means cold, one would stay inside and miss the opportunity to relieve some stress, get some fresh air, and improve health by taking a walk outdoors on that 50° day.

The dialectic applied to life situations can free us from rigidity. It allows us to adapt to changing circumstances in such a way that optimizes life experiences. The implications of this kind of adaptability are virtually limitless. When practiced regularly it permeates all of one's thinking, enabling one to transform any situation to the understanding of one's choosing. On a hot summer day it's going be much easier to adapt to that temperature if one eats a slice of watermelon rather than a bowl of hot stew. The watermelon is cooling, making one comfortable on a hot day. While a cup of hot stew is very nourishing, it might not be the best energy on a hot day to help one adapt to the heat.

Using the dialectic and learning to be adaptable is not easy. The dialectic and the adaptability it provides enables us to transform a circumstance into something of our choosing. To me this is freedom. This is empowerment. This is what a macrobiotic practice can do.

Chapter 19

See for Yourself

The freedom to determine for oneself is central to human uniqueness and dignity. This is the most effective way to make a choice that is appropriate for one's personal condition. If the words of a teacher, the advice of a counselor, or the ideas of a book crowd out one's own judgment, the result is not as good as it could be.

George Ohsawa, by all accounts, was a charismatic and forceful personality. There are many stories of how he would "train" his students to think for themselves. Ohsawa would lecture, pose questions, and reward the response that came from a student's original thinking. Even as Ohsawa taught the order of the universe, I imagine he charged his students to "see for yourself." This is one of the most important concepts of Ohsawa's legacy to the world. He was very specific in many of his teachings and very demanding of his students, often scolding them severely for "parroted" answers or failures of discipline.

At heart, Ohsawa's greatest concern was to teach his students how to think for themselves. He lamented that the world was populated with rote parroting automatons. He saw the lack of thinking for oneself as an underlying reason for people's sickness and misery. Further, he claimed that one's condition resulted directly from the manner in which one conducts his/her daily life. Every decision we make—from the smallest seemingly trivial mundane choice to the most major life altering choice—determines what condition we either enjoy or suffer. Those choices are determined by our judgment. Develop good judgment and one can enjoy a happy healthy life. Good judgment creates freedom.

Take macrobiotic theory and practice and make it your own. That to me is the legacy of George Ohsawa. If you come across any aspect of theory or practice that just doesn't seem quite right in your heart and mind: ask questions, debate theory, and experiment with alternative ideas and practices. But don't take my or anybody else's word for it. Try it and see!

Good Judgment—Good Decisions

George Ohsawa elaborated on seven levels of judgment. If interested, there are several books that describe the seven levels of judgment in great detail. The point is the importance of judgment in all things. Judgment (one's judging ability) is what enables us to make decisions that promote health and well-being in regard to diet, lifestyle, vocation or relationships. Good judgment enables one to transform any situation to one's advantage, to learn from a challenge and become stronger and better for it. Good judgment enables one not to be intimidated by any form of status or authority. Good judgment enables one to be able to see through the smoke screen of illusion or misdirection and to see the truth of the matter or of a person. With clarity comes truth, with truth comes good judgment, with good judgment comes good decisions and the power to transform. One is able to harness the dynamics of change and create the world of one's vision.

Ohsawa put forward many philosophical ideas. One of his most profound and enduring ideas is the notion of personal freedom that he claimed is achievable through macrobiotic practice. I wrote earlier about freedom achieved through the respect of limitations. His thinking was that if one respects one's limitations, there is infinite freedom within those limitations. Conversely, if one exceeded those limitations, one becomes a slave to the compensations and accommodations that are necessary to restore balance.

An example that each of us can relate to is with food. If we are eating devitalized, processed food, heavy with excess fat, protein, salt, sugar, and chemicals, it is highly likely that we will develop symptoms ranging from aches and pains to headaches and digestions problems, moodiness, and in the extreme heart disease, diabetes, and cancer. However, if we truly use macrobiotic principles in our diets and lifestyle choices; and, if we learn to respect our limitations about what and how much to eat, we would be much less likely to develop these disorders.

Macrobiotic Principles Are Not Enough

While macrobiotic principles are guides that provide a place to start, everything depends on the quality of one's decisions—good judgment. Good judgment begins with mental clarity. If we can't see things as they really are, we are living in a fog of illusion and nothing will turn out as we expect. If we believe that a no-carb, high protein/fat diet will enable us to lose weight, and we lack the clarity to notice the development of constipation at the same time, we become confused. Yet, because someone else said it would work, we override our own judgment and clarity and think, "I should be healthy," but the constipation doesn't improve. We are "slaves" not only to the symptom of constipation, but to the rigidity of mind that prevents us from making a personal, appropriate, and healthy decision—a decision that could relieve the constipation and lead to the truth that this no-carb, high fat/protein dietary approach doesn't work.

Another example common in macrobiotic and vegan/vegetarian circles is the limiting of fat and protein. Well-intentioned, intelligent people motivated by commendable principles willfully limit themselves to a diet with insufficient nutrition thinking they are being spiritual and saving the planet. When symptoms of imbalance develop—in this case it would likely be symptoms of deficiency, e.g. weakness, fatigue, excess weight loss, disruption of reproductive function—the zealousness of conviction clouds judgment. Not seeing clearly what is truly happening and not truly acknowledging and acting on one's biofeedback can result in deteriorating health.

It seems to me Ohsawa would be quite surprised to see how so many people easily gave away their freedom to choose and submitted to the dictates of overbearing teachers and counselors or rigid dogma.

People who stifle their own judgment, their own clear thinking, and their own truth and remain dependent upon teachers and counselors may become the very slaves that he cautioned against.

Chapter 20

Free at Last

Freedom through Macrobiotics

One day back in the early 1990s, I was walking down the hall at the Vega Study Center when seemingly out of nowhere Herman Aihara stopped me and asked point blank, "What do you get from Ohsawa?" Talk about being put on the spot! When I initially sifted through George Ohsawa's writings, I was a bit overwhelmed by the sweep of his ideas. He talked about so many areas: cosmic, social, economic, political, physical health and medical systems, as well as spiritual traditions from the Bible to the Bhagavad-Gita. With Herman standing right there in front of my face I thought for a moment or maybe I didn't think, and what I came up with was, "Freedom."

I don't know what Herman expected me to say, but he looked surprised. Then in his inimitable fashion, he nodded his head up-and-down, turned, and walked away leaving me standing there somewhat dumbfounded. To this day I don't really know what that was about, but that moment has stuck with me ever since. So much so, that when I talk about Ohsawa, I talk about freedom.

My personal interest in macrobiotics (and TCM too) has always been primarily philosophical and spiritual. My take is that macrobiotics is fundamentally a spiritual practice supported by physical dietary and lifestyle practices. I am moved by the teachings in macrobiotics that refer to freedom, Big Life, realizing one's dream/inspiration/purpose—the melding of spiritual insight and physical harmony. I believe this is a winning combination.

Ohsawa wrote and taught about many areas. I consider his

most valuable contribution to humanity to be the teaching of how to develop good judgment. He taught the importance of personal integrity and how to be honest with one's self, to know one's own mind, and to be able to get in touch with one's unique voice. Finding one's unique voice enables one to discover one's true purpose. Aligning with one's true purpose leads to the realization of one's true destiny. I believe one's true destiny represents fulfillment, oneness, and wholeness. The achievement of oneness in physical life is the highest experience available to us. It is the melding of the physical and spiritual dimensions.

To experience oneness requires clarity and critical thinking. Describing Ohsawa's teaching style, Herman would often say that Ohsawa rewarded original thinking and scolded students whose answers smacked of what the teacher expected. Ohsawa taught students how to think for themselves. Over the years I have come to believe that thinking for oneself, i.e. developing good judgment, is one of the essential and primary tools for realizing optimum health, realizing one's dream, and experiencing oneness, wholeness, and fulfillment.

Essentially, I believe Ohsawa taught his students how to strive for clear thinking and to make that thinking their own. The following is what I see as the key elements of how to develop clear thinking, critical thinking, and good judgment.

I. Stabilize Physiology

We all live in the physical dimension. The physical dimension is very dense compared to the energetic and spiritual dimensions. When the physical dimension is not harmonized, it is difficult to access the spiritual dimension. Without being able to access the spiritual dimension, realizing one's true destiny and fulfillment in this life is nearly impossible. The place to start in developing good judgment is to consciously stabilize one's physiology. In this endeavor, macrobiotic dietary and lifestyle practices are enormously helpful.

The choices we make in our physical practices can create

imbalances. These imbalances can result in constant distractions. Ohsawa taught that we must understand and respect our limits. If we stay within our limits we can experience infinite freedom, if we exceed our limits we will be imprisoned—literally slaves to our excesses or our deficiencies.

Macrobiotic practices support balance and stability of physiology. Studying and learning macrobiotic dietary and lifestyle principles and conscientiously applying these principles over time can help to stabilize one's physiology. Indeed, macrobiotic theory and practice are all about balance, harmony, grounded-ness, and in turn stability…physiological stability.

When one's physiology is stabilized, then physiology is not (at least is less of) a distraction. One is freed from the energy consuming activity of recovering from imbalances. The enormous amount of mental and physical energy needed to restore balance can now be directed to perceiving and receiving inspirations from the Divine.

With the energy that is freed up from stabilized physiology, it is possible to:

- Know one's true purpose
- Realize one's dream
- Experience enlightenment—to be aligned with Qi/Prana/ animating force of the Universe, Tao, Satori
- Eat and drink anything with pleasure
- Be Free

II. Cultivate Mindfulness

Mindfulness is a crucial element in the evolution of consciousness and the creation of good judgment. With mindfulness comes clarity, with clarity one can see one's personal truth, knowing personal truth leads to one's true destiny, and in the pursuit of one's true destiny one advances to a higher state of being.

Modern life is filled with delusion and seduction. We only have to look at advertising to see how we are invited to invest in illusions in the pursuit of satisfaction or other positive outcomes. Surely if a man drinks this beer or smokes that cigarette he will become a real man. Or if a woman uses this perfume or that brand of make up she will become as beautiful as a movie star. With mindfulness and a clear perception of what is (reality)—we aren't fooled by illusion or seduced by hype.

Mindfulness also helps us develop the power of discernment. For example, we know with certainty what food to eat, when to eat, and how much to eat. No teacher/counselor/book has to tell us—we know, and only each of us knows for ourselves. This is what is meant by knowing one's personal truth and discovering one's unique voice. With mindfulness and clarity we can see and know our personal truth in any circumstance no matter what anyone else says. We may consider the opinions of others but at best they are secondary. As it pertains to one's discernment, one's truth is primary.

Lies/deceptions/illusions are shaky/slippery. It takes a lot of energy to remember all our lies and to persuade ourselves that a deception is the truth. And ultimately, it is not convincing anyway. With lies and deception as a basis for decision making it is hard to make substantive change. There is nothing solid to push off from to make a decision and initiate an action. The basis for the decision and action is shifting sands and squishy. Rather than pushing off, we sink as if in quicksand and we are ultimately revealed as a fraud. Truth is solid: from a basis of truth, constructive, productive, transformative change happens. In truth, energy and relationships are clean and all variables are known accurately so that an action taken has a high probability of effective execution.

III. Develop Discipline

I remember Cornellia Aihara's description of macrobiotic practice. She would say that practicing macrobiotics is not complicated, that actually it is simple; however, to get results one's macrobiotic practice must be specific and uncompromising. I think this succinctly captures the role of discipline in good judgment.

Considering physical health, our current condition is a combination of our constitution and the cumulative effect of all our past choices. We study, learn, practice, develop, and grow in our lives to acquire the knowledge and skills to experience good health and to realize our true destiny. We are always striving to make better choices. We simply have to have discipline to stick with it. Discipline is necessary to sustain healthy constructive development. It's not complicated, but it is specific and uncompromising and it takes discipline to be specific and uncompromising in our choices.

One suggestion in terms of improving discipline is a simple sequence of changing an undesirablc or unproductive pattern into a desirable and productive one. Say you have been eating pressure cooked short grain brown rice that is a little on the salty side hoping that your digestion would improve; but, it's just not happening. Something doesn't feel right. Here are suggestions on how to embark on a journey of discovery and change.

Clarity and Change

Step 1: Clearly recognize and acknowledge that what you are doing isn't working.

Step 2: STOP what you're doing that doesn't work.

Step 3: Reflect and analyze—with reflection/analysis you can gain understanding about what's not working.

Step 4: Then when you understand what isn't working, you can make a conscious new choice that will change the pattern from unproductive too productive.

Let's apply this to our example of eating salty pressure cooked short grain brown rice. One day you're chewing away on a big pile of the short grain rice and sense tightness in your stomach. Instead of overriding that tightness because a counselor told you that short grain brown rice is the best rice for you, you acknowledge that it has made your stomach feel tight. So you stop. Then you think to yourself, perhaps the texture and energy of this kind of rice is not the best for me. From this analysis you decide to try something different. You decide to try some less salty steamed/boiled basmati brown rice and after eating it your stomach does not feel tight. Discipline can support good judgment and empower you to break out of old patterns. Be specific and uncompromising in your creativity as you build your diet and lifestyle practices.

IV. Have Faith, Belief, Confidence, and Courage

When we start out on our journey of discovery in life, we are likely on another's path. One may have followed the teachings of any of the thousands of teachers, gurus, seers, and masters from Jesus and Buddha to Herman Aihara and Michio Kushi. It is an obvious place to start. In the early stages of our growth and development we need information, skills, and guidance. During that stage of one's life it is helpful and productive to follow an established way of thinking or way of doing things. However, as we develop and begin to discover our own personal truth and unique individual voice, it may become increasingly difficult to stay within the parameters of the person or system we followed when we were younger.

It is my observation that someone who remains committed to personal growth and evolution may eventually reach the point where he/she must depart and move beyond the system he/she followed earlier on. At this point, one must begin to define one's life experience in one's own creative terms. One may literally have to make it up as one goes along. Again I take inspiration from Herman Aihara. The master/student tradition in Japan is such that a student doesn't challenge the master's teachings. I believe the spirit of George Ohsawa's teaching overturns this tradition and Herman Aihara understood that. Herman expanded Ohsawa's thinking on acid and alkaline as I mentioned before. Ohsawa's formulation was that when comparing acid and alkaline, an acid is yin and an alkaline is yang. Herman put forward the idea that an acid could be either yin or yang and that an alkaline also could be either yin or yang. See Herman's masterwork *Acid and Alkaline* for more details of how he modified and extended Ohsawa's ideas about acid and alkaline. This is a perfect example of what I'm describing in this section. If one's truth guides one to something different than what is established, then one must follow it to be true to oneself.

No one can know another person's deepest intimate thoughts

and feelings. Only that person can make decisions for him- or herself that are perfectly customized to who he or she is. And, one can only do that with clarity, truth, and discipline. The path to one's freedom eventually must be unique and individual. To realize the merging of physical and spiritual dimensions, one must discover one's true purpose and true destiny. Then, the state of being that is pointed to by all the great religions and philosophies and variously known as Heaven, Paradise, Nirvana, or Enlightenment can be realized.

Traversing the Unknown

The challenge in moving from following another's path to creating one's own path is that one has to enter into and traverse the unknown. When one leaves one's teacher's path, one exits the familiar and generally acknowledged path and steps into the unknown where there might not be a teacher, master, or guidance in the sense that one has always known. One realizes that he or she will have to create it by him or her self. If one has truly qualified oneself for this opportunity by this time, one will be able to receive guidance and teaching directly from the Divine, Qi, Prana, or Life Force itself. I believe this is the most exhilarating experience available to us as human beings—channeling pure life force through one's body, mind, and spirit to make life-giving contributions to the universe. Furthermore, decisions made in truth and actions taken in truth draw the support of the divine energetic/spiritual dimensions and provide material resources—be they physical health, financial means, or real world opportunities—for the successful realization of these decisions.

During this time, and forever after, we will be challenged. To continue to survive and thrive we must develop belief, faith, and confidence in ourselves. We may waver, but should never turn away from or deny our inspirations, perceptions, judgment, actions, thoughts, and dreams because we know in our heart of hearts that if we believe, have faith, and maintain confidence, that all will come to good. It must because if we are channeling pure life force, the consequences are surely more life and more creation to sustain the vitality of the universe. If we have belief, faith, and confidence, we will find the courage to overcome obstacles and resist naysayers, critics, and teasers. We can pursue and act upon our truth, which, I repeat, will be personally fulfilling and a life-giving contribution to the vitality of the universe.

V. Summary

To my way of thinking, one of the most profound and beneficial goals of macrobiotic theory and practice is freedom:

- Freedom from physiological distraction.
- Freedom from being chained to another's path.
- Freedom to discover/define one's unique path/purpose/mission in this life.
- Freedom to connect with one's true personal unique karmic, spiritual, and physical destiny.
- Freedom to pursue and realize the wholeness, oneness, and apex of fulfillment in life.
- Freedom to experience Oneness with the Divine, God, Heaven, Paradise, Nirvana, Enlightenment.

And then, in the immortal words of the Rev. Dr. Martin Luther King Jr., we are "Free at last, Free at last, Thank God almighty we are free at last."

Chapter 21

Gratitude

I am grateful to all of the teachers, counselors, cooks, merchants, farmers, and everyone else involved with macrobiotics for all the work they have done to make macrobiotics available all these years. I especially acknowledge Herman and Cornellia Aihara for giving me the opportunity to work in macrobiotics and for the confidence and trust they placed in me to play a role in seeing that it continues.

Particularly, I am grateful to Hermann for giving me free rein as editor of *Macrobiotics Today*. He never once spoke a word of restriction about any of the work that I did. Exemplifying "see for yourself" by putting his own stamp on macrobiotic theory with his work on acid and alkaline set the tone for the ideas I have put forward here.

I have sought to identify the areas of macrobiotics that are great contributions to civilization. And I have sought to identify the areas of macrobiotics that might benefit from discussion, debate, and possible modification. Hopefully, macrobiotics will be of even greater value to more people in the future.

I am grateful for having connected with macrobiotics in my life. It has been a long time now, but I recall that my days before I found macrobiotics were chaotic. I had no "magic spectacles." I had no guiding principles, particularly in diet and lifestyle. Working with macrobiotics over the years I have found my way, I have found my purpose, and I can honestly say that I have a fulfilling life.

In closing, I would once again like to express my heartfelt gratitude to George and Lima Ohsawa, Herman and Cornellia Aihara, Michio and Aveline Kushi, and the many macrobiotic teachers around the world who have preserved and nurtured the precious teachings of macrobiotics.

Macrobiotics has made the world a better place.

The Author

Bob Ligon worked at the Vega Study Center and George Ohsawa Macrobiotic Foundation from 1989-1993 and was the editor of *Macrobiotics Today* from 1992-2000. He studied acupuncture and herbology graduating from Pacific College of Oriental Medicine in San Diego in 1998. He integrates his knowledge of macrobiotics and Chinese Medicine in his diet, lifestyle counseling, and life coaching. Currently, Bob practices Traditional Chinese Medicine in Akron, Ohio.

A list of books by George Ohsawa and others on macrobiotics can be obtained from the George Ohsawa Macrobiotic Foundation, PO Box 3998, Chico, CA 95927-3998; *gomf@earthlink.net;* 530-566-9765. Or, visit *www.OhsawaMacrobiotics.com.*

Made in the USA
Lexington, KY
15 November 2017